Aural Matters
In Practice

Advanced Tests in Aural Perception based on *The Essential Hyperion*

David Bowman
and
Paul Terry

ED 12441

SCHOTT

Mainz · London · Madrid · New York · Paris · Prag · Tokyo · Toronto
© 1994 SCHOTT & Co. Ltd., London · Printed in Germany

The authors and publisher would like to thank Hyperion Records Ltd for kindly granting permission for this book to be based on their anthology of recorded highlights, *The Essential Hyperion* (HYP12).

Thanks are also due to Rosalie Wilding for her translation of the poem by Metastasio (Test 20) and to Dom Andrew McAffrey, OSB, for his translation of Aquinas (Test 19).

Test 16: Prelude No. 7 in A by Dimitri Shostakovich
© Copyright 1955 by Leeds Music Corp.
Reproduced by permission of Boosey & Hawkes Music Publishers Ltd.

British Library Cataloguing-in-Publication Data.
A catalogue record for this book is available from the British Library.

ISBN 0 946535 23 X

ED 12441
© 1994 Schott & Co. Ltd, London

Typeset by Musonix Typesetting

Introduction

This book, with its accompanying compact disc, provides aural training materials to supplement the exercises in Part II of *Aural Matters*, also by David Bowman and Paul Terry, published by Schott & Co. Ltd. *Aural Matters* is primarily a resource to help students improve their own aural perception and stylistic awareness of music. *Aural Matters In Practice* has been written at the request of many teachers seeking additional materials to use in class, both to monitor progress and provide further practice in working formal tests. The book has accordingly been designed with space for students' responses, and with model answers (and suggested marks) printed on the centre folios for easy removal if desired.

The musical examples are complementary to those in *Aural Matters*. Some focus on related material while others provide an opportunity to investigate styles and genres for which there was insufficient room to explore in full in the original volume. It is not intended that the tests in this book should, on their own, provide complete coverage of all the styles that students will need to encounter for examinations. In particular, it will be seen that the accompanying compact disc does not include examples of jazz, folk or world music. However, a wide variety of techniques and forms is encompassed by the tests, including many that are of relevance to these other types of music.

The tests are, for convenience, numbered to match the tracks on the accompanying compact disc. They can be worked in this order, although an alternative Scheme of Work is suggested on the centre pages. A few of the extracts are longer than might be expected in examinations. For these, we have suggested convenient places where the music can be divided into more manageable sections for aural analysis and have set separate tests on each of these shorter passages. Tests 8 and 9 are based on earlier music than that generally included in examination syllabuses at this level. Questions on these two pieces have therefore been designed to relate only to technical features which are common to other types of music.

It is suggested that, for examination practice purposes, the music for each test should be played three times, with reading time at the start and a silence of one minute between playings. However, in the earlier stages of aural training extra playings will be beneficial in helping candidates to focus on detailed listening without the pressure of limited time. The authors wish to stress the value of always listening to the music again, after the answers have been noted, to ensure that any musical techniques that were missed during the test can, in fact, be recognized *in the music* once they have been pointed out. In most cases, any unfamiliar terms or concepts can be looked up in the index of *Aural Matters*, which will indicate further examples to be found in the text of that book and illustrated among its associated recordings.

The recordings

Each of the tests in this book is based on the related recording of the music on the accompanying compact disc from Hyperion Records Ltd, *The Essential Hyperion*. This includes more than one and a quarter hours of music, and many of the recordings will also be useful for providing additional material to illustrate the examples in *Aural Matters* (see the Scheme of Work on the centre pages).

The complete works from which the extracts are taken are available from Hyperion Records Ltd. Titles, catalogue numbers and other details of these are given in the CD insert booklet.

Also available

This book is intended to supplement the resources provided in *Aural Matters, A Student's Guide to Aural Perception at Advanced Level* (Schott & Co. Ltd, 1993), with its accompanying anthology of 154 extracts of recorded music: ED 12430 Book with two compact discs.

Readers are also referred to *Sound Matters* (Schott & Co. Ltd, 1989), an anthology of 72 extracts of printed and recorded music, available with teacher's manual and pupils' questions: ED 12351 Score, ED 12353 Two compact disks or cassettes, ED 12352 Teacher's manual (with pupils' questions).

World Sound Matters (Schott & Co. Ltd, 1996) is a fully-integrated anthology of music from around the world. The compact discs contain 58 recordings of traditional music from 35 countries, the music book has an annotated transcription of each recorded example and the teacher's manual includes two sets of listening-based pupils' questions: ED 12460 Teacher's manual and pupils' questions, ED 12571 Music book, ED 12572 Two compact discs.

The orchestral movement on Track 1 starts with the following trumpet music:

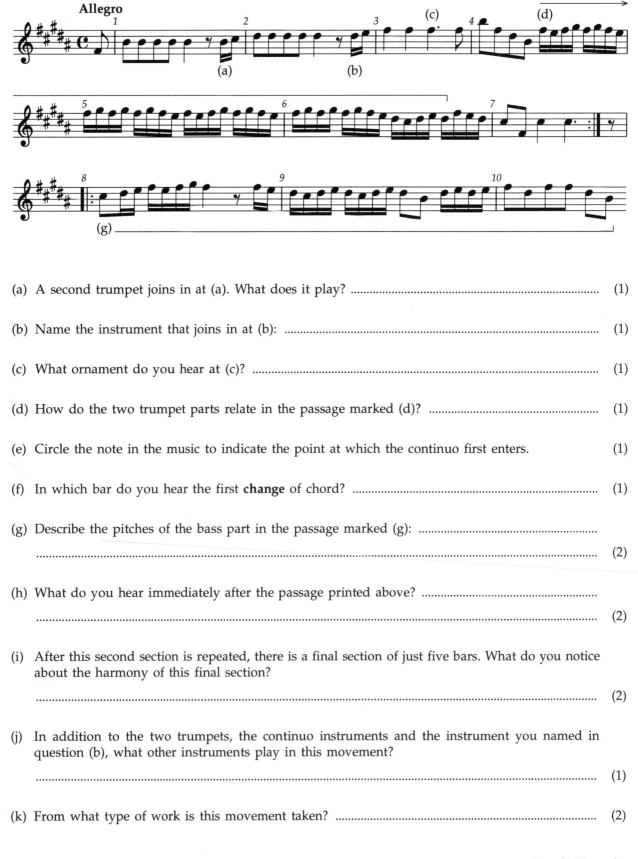

(a) A second trumpet joins in at (a). What does it play? .... (1)

(b) Name the instrument that joins in at (b): .... (1)

(c) What ornament do you hear at (c)? .... (1)

(d) How do the two trumpet parts relate in the passage marked (d)? .... (1)

(e) Circle the note in the music to indicate the point at which the continuo first enters. (1)

(f) In which bar do you hear the first **change** of chord? .... (1)

(g) Describe the pitches of the bass part in the passage marked (g): ....

.... (2)

(h) What do you hear immediately after the passage printed above? ....

.... (2)

(i) After this second section is repeated, there is a final section of just five bars. What do you notice about the harmony of this final section?

.... (2)

(j) In addition to the two trumpets, the continuo instruments and the instrument you named in question (b), what other instruments play in this movement?

.... (1)

(k) From what type of work is this movement taken? .... (2)

Total: 15 marks

[4]

This *rondeau* consists of seven clearly defined sections in the following pattern:

A	A	B	A	C	A	A

Each section consists of an eight-bar phrase in triple time.

(a) In section A:

    (i)   Describe the opening four-note figure of the melody:

    .... (2)

    (ii) Describe, as fully as you can, the melodic patterns heard in the middle of this melody:

    .... (3)

    (iii) Describe the rhythmic patterns in the last two bars of this melody:

    .... (1)

(b) In section B:

    (i)   How do the first two bars of this section relate to the first two bars of section A?

    .... (1)

    (ii) In what other way is the melody of this section similar to the melody of section A?

    .... (1)

(c) In section C:

    (i)   Describe **one** way in which this whole melody differs from the melody of section A:

    .... (1)

    (ii) Describe **two** ways in which the tonality of this section differs from the tonality of section B:

    .... (2)

(d) Briefly describe the texture and instrumentation of the whole *rondeau:*

....

....

.... (4)

Total: 15 marks

[5]

The song on this track is a setting of the following text:

1. A prince of glorious race descended,   } *repeated*
2. At his happy birth attended,
3. With rosy smiling hours to show
4. He will golden days bestow.

In addition to the repetition of lines 1 and 2 in their entirety, various individual words and phrases are repeated throughout the setting.

Archlute

(a) Name the three continuo instruments that accompany the singer:

Arch lute · viol Bassoon cello - organ (3)

(b) How does the composer highlight the word 'glorious' in line 1?

melisma   Glo-or-o. Melisma (1)

(c) How does the singer alter the melody for the words 'A prince' when line 1 is repeated in its entirety?

First note class. up to second prince (1)

(d) Describe the melodic patterns in the bass part during lines 1 and 2 and their repeat:

Major   sequence descend .... *I ... triads* (3)

(e) How do these melodic patterns in the bass differ in line 3?

Ascending: modulation to dominant Major (1)

(f) What does the music of line 4 have in common with that of line 1?

Back to Tonic key. Same bass part (1)

(g) Describe the ritornello for strings and continuo which forms the second half of this extract:

Melody of singer not ornamented repeated (1)

(h) What compositional technique is used throughout most of this track? *Ostinato (Ground bass)* (1)

(i) Suggest the name of the composer of this music: *Purcell. Baroque.*

and the approximate date of its composition: *1612 - 1695* (2)

Melisma e.g. glo-o-o-o-or

Singinging lots of notes one syllable

Total: 14 marks

[6]

The music on this track consists of the opening arioso from a secular cantata. It begins with an orchestral introduction based on the following melody:

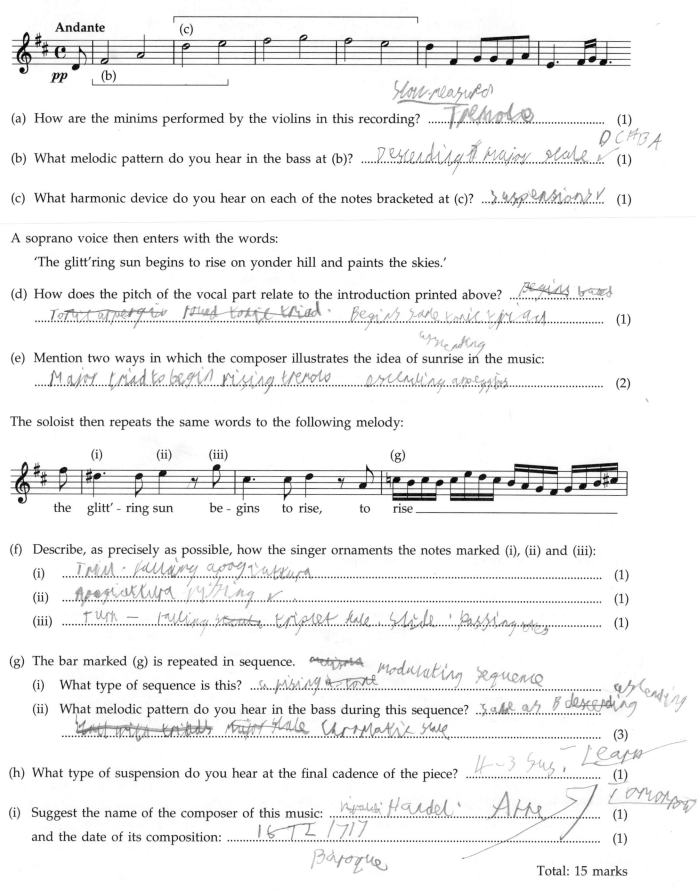

(a) How are the minims performed by the violins in this recording? *Slow measured Tremolo* (1)

(b) What melodic pattern do you hear in the bass at (b)? *Descending major scale* *D C#B A* (1)

(c) What harmonic device do you hear on each of the notes bracketed at (c)? *Suspensions* (1)

A soprano voice then enters with the words:

'The glitt'ring sun begins to rise on yonder hill and paints the skies.'

(d) How does the pitch of the vocal part relate to the introduction printed above? *Begins bass* *Tonic arpeggio found tonic triad. Begins same tonic up an 8th* (1)

(e) Mention two ways in which the composer illustrates the idea of sunrise in the music:
Major triad to begin rising tremolo *ascending* *ascending arpeggios* (2)

The soloist then repeats the same words to the following melody:

(f) Describe, as precisely as possible, how the singer ornaments the notes marked (i), (ii) and (iii):

   (i) *Trill. falling appoggiatura* (1)

   (ii) *Appoggiatura rising* (1)

   (iii) *Turn — falling triplet scale slide. passing notes* (1)

(g) The bar marked (g) is repeated in sequence. *modulating sequence*

   (i) What type of sequence is this? *rising a tone* *ascending* (3)

   (ii) What melodic pattern do you hear in the bass during this sequence? *Same as B descending* *tonic triad major scale Chromatic scale.*

(h) What type of suspension do you hear at the final cadence of the piece? *4–3 sus. Learn tomorrow* (1)

(i) Suggest the name of the composer of this music: *Vivaldi Handel. Arne* (1)

   and the date of its composition: *16TI /1717* (1)

Baroque

Total: 15 marks

[handwritten at top: L Listen again for modulations and cadences]

Here is the text of the operatic excerpt, sung in English, on this track:

1. *Father:*   Thus old wits, in wicked satires, formerly the fair maligned;
    Called them light, false, vain, affected, and unsteady as the wind.
    If they copied after nature, blessed are English dames I trow,
    So much altered from what ladies were two thousand years ago.

   Refrain: If they copied after nature, blessed are English dames I trow,
    So much altered from what ladies were two thousand years ago.

2. *Maid:*   Mean and false the accusation. Men our sex unjustly blame;
    They are slaves to little passions, and would brand us with the same.
    Struck with native imperfection as their mind the object sours,
    From themselves they draw a picture, then cry out 'the face is ours!'

   Refrain: Struck with native imperfection as their mind the object sours,
    From themselves they draw a picture, then cry out 'the face is ours!'

3. *Matron:*   Says the traveller to a lion: 'Up on yonder signpost see
    How a lion like your worship's torn by a man like me.'
    Says the lion to the traveller, ''Twas a man the daubing drew;
    Had a lion been the painter I had been a-tearing you'.

   Refrain: Says the lion to the traveller, ''Twas a man the daubing drew;
    Had a lion been the painter I had been a-tearing you'.

4. *Centurion:* No excuses or allusions: here's the burden of my song;
    Women sovereigns are of nature (and as such can do no wrong).
    Sent to bless, to rule, to charm us, angels all of grace and light,
    Everything they say is proper, everything they do is right.

   Refrain: Sent to bless, to rule, to charm us, angels all of grace and light,
    Everything they say is proper, everything they do is right.   *(repeated)*

(a) Here is the melody of the short introduction, heard before verse 1:

Describe, as precisely as possible, the instrumentation of phrase (a) and its accompaniment:

[handwritten: ...2 Horns + 7 Strings + oboe. bassoon]

.... (3)

(b) Complete the following brief descriptions of the solo in each verse:

   (i)   Verse 1 is sung by a solo baritone.

      The voice is accompanied throughout by: ...*[handwritten: strings ✓]*............. (1)

      The music modulates from the tonic to: ...*[handwritten: Minor (Dominant) tonic]*........ (1)

[8]

(ii) Verse 2 is sung by a solo: ...*Soprano*... (1)

In the first half of the verse the voice is accompanied by: ...*2 horns oboes* ✓... (1)

In the second half of the verse the harmonic progressions are all: ...*modulating so*... ...*Dominant chord* *Major modulating sequences*... (2) ✓

(iii) Verse 3 is sung by a solo: ...*M: Soprano* ✓... (1)

The first half of the verse modulates from the tonic to: ...*dominant — to keys*... (1)

The second half of the verse has a melody consisting almost entirely of: ...*repeating*... ...*sequence major scale patterns. conjunct motion* ✓... (1)

(iv) Verse 4 is sung by a solo: ...*Alto Tenor* ✓... (1)

The harmonization of most of the verse is based on: ...*The introduction* ✓ *Recur*... (1)

Instead of modulating, the verse ends with the following type of cadence: ...*plagal*... (1)

(c) (i) What music is used for the refrains to verses 1–3? ...*The introduction* ✓...
.... (1)

(ii) Describe the vocal texture in these refrains: ...*Homophonic* ✓... (1)

(iii) What new vocal texture is heard in the extended refrain following verse 4? ...*Antiphony*...
...*Alternate voices*... (1)

(iv) Which of the following chords do you hear immediately before the final perfect cadence of the entire piece?

chord IIb   (G sharp minor/B)

chord IV   (B)

chord V   (C sharp)

the dominant of the dominant   (G sharp)

a cadential 6–4   (F sharp/C sharp)

a diminished seventh   (dim. 7)

.... *cadential* .... (1)

(d) Suggest a date when you believe this music was written: ...*1762* *V V* ✓... (1)

Total: 20 marks

[9]

Listen to the first part of the music on Track 6, stopping at the word 'Israel' in the text below (there is a silence at this point, 2'38" into the track). After a short introduction on the organ, the opening melody is sung by a treble soloist:

My soul ____ doth mag - ni - fy the Lord, ____ And my spi - rit hath re - joiced

Use the following text to identify the features mentioned in questions (a) to (e):

1. My soul doth magnify the Lord,
2. And my spirit hath rejoiced in God my Saviour.
3. For he hath regarded the lowliness of his handmaiden,
4. For behold from henceforth all generations shall call me blessed.
5. For he that is mighty hath magnified me; and holy is his name.
6. And his mercy is on them that fear him, throughout all generations.
7. He hath showed strength with his arm,
8. He hath scattered the proud in the imagination of their hearts,
9. He hath put down the mighty from their seat, and hath exalted the humble and meek.
10. He hath filled the hungry with good things and the rich he hath sent empty away,
11. He remembering his mercy, hath holpen his servant Israel.

(a) Write down the words of the text where you can hear:

   (i) A repetition of the phrase marked *x* in the music above:
        For behold ... he that is mighty (1)

   (ii) Imitation based on the phrase marked *y* in the music above:
        Holy is his his name (1)

(b) In the setting of line 4, describe:

   (i) The bass part in the first half of the line ('For behold from henceforth all generations'):
        It is first a quiet pedal sustained under Arpeggios (2)

   (ii) The melodic ornament each time the word 'blessed' is sung: *Appoggiatura* (1)

(c) In the setting of line 8, describe the texture at the words 'in the imagination of their hearts':
    Homophonic text Homophonic polyphonic sparse.
    Descant harmony - Two voices. No organ. Triplophone (3)

(d) In the setting of line 11, describe:

   (i) the relationship of the solo part to the underlying harmonies at the words 'He remembering his mercy': *Dim*
        There is a dissonant interval - A suspension. Dissonance (2)

   (ii) the relationship of the choral treble part to the preceding solo part at the words 'hath holpen his servant': *It is an exact imitation a third descending sequence)* (1)

(e) Describe the predominant figure heard in the organ part throughout most of this extract:
    A first descending and ascending Arpeggio sequence (3)
    alternating between chords I and V

Total: 14 marks

[10]

Now listen to the remainder of the piece, starting after the silence at a point 2'39" into the track. Follow the words below and answer questions (f) to (j):

1. As he promised to our forefathers,
2. Abraham and his seed for ever.
3. Glory be to the Father, and to the Son, and to the Holy Ghost;
4. As it was in the beginning, is now, and ever shall be,
5. World without end. Amen.

(f) Write down the words of the above text where you can hear:

   (i) A reference to the first two bars of the music printed opposite:

      our father   (1)

   (ii) A reference to the passage marked *y* in the music printed opposite:

      seed for ever   (1)

(g) Describe the vocal texture at the words 'Glory be to the Father, and to the Son' in line 3:

   Homophonic. In unison.   (2)

(h) Name the cadence at the end of:

   (i) line 3: *Imperfect V-6*   (1)

   (ii) line 4: *Interrupted*   (1)

   (iii) line 5: *Plagal*   (1)

(i) In lines 3–5:

   (i) How does the metre differ from the rest of the music on this track?   (1)

   (ii) How does the organ accompaniment differ from the rest of the music? *It follows the tune sung homophonically in block chords.*   (1)

(j) This music was written by Stanford in 1903. To which of the following composers do you think his style is most indebted?

(Byrd)

Bach

Beethoven

Berlioz

Wagner

Brahms

Debussy   (1)

Total: 10 marks

The music on this track consists of a setting of the following text for *a capella* choir:

Solo sung to plainsong: 1. *Libera nos,*   Deliver us,
Choir: 2. *Salva nos,*   Save us,
    3. *Justifica nos,*   Give us justice,
    4. *O beata Trinitas.*   O blessed Trinity.

(a) Line 1 is sung to plainsong by a soloist. The plainsong melody then continues throughout the rest of the piece as a cantus firmus. Which choral part sings it?

.... (1)

(b) How many voice parts are there in all? .... (1)

(c) Lines 2, 3 and 4 are each based on the imitative treatment of one or more short motifs. These are printed below as they first appear in the uppermost voice, but not in the order in which they occur. Under each motif write the line number in which it is sung, remembering that one of the lines includes two of these motifs:

(i) Line number: ....

(ii) Line number: ....

(iii) Line number: ....

(iv) Line number: ....

(4)

(d) How does the composer achieve continuity between these four points of imitation?

.... (1)

(e) Which of the following occurs at the final cadence?

appoggiatura   antiphony   consonant fourth

tierce de Picardie   suspension   melodic sequence   .... (1)

(f) Which of the following best describes the tonality of this music?

diatonic major

major with modulations to related keys

major with occasional flattened sevenths

Dorian mode

Dorian mode with occasional false relations

Aeolian mode   .... (1)

(g) In which century was this music written? .... (1)

Total: 10 marks

A Note on Tests 8 and 9

The song on Track 8 dates from the 13th century and the *chanson* on Track 9 was written in the 15th century. Examination syllabuses that prescribe the study of music from 1550 onwards will not, of course, include such early pieces as these. However, there is no need to restrict your enjoyment of music to the styles and periods set for examination. While both pieces include some features that you may not have encountered before, all of the questions are concerned with concepts that should be familiar from the study of other types of music. The notes below should help you to place both pieces in context.

Test 8: *Mandad' ei comigo*

This song, by Martin Codax, most probably dates from the years around 1270—over a century before Chaucer's *Canterbury Tales* and more than 300 years before Shakespeare wrote his first play. It is thus from among the earliest periods of music whose notation can still be understood, although there is some doubt about the precise interpretation of rhythm at this time. The original manuscript was only discovered in 1914, packed into the binding of a book. Like much secular music of the period, it gives only the text and the melody—all of the other parts have been recreated in the modern performance on the recording.

The realization of this type of medieval music is often similar to folk music—compare this song with some of the examples of folk music in *Aural Matters*, particularly those that are also modal and realized with a drone and percussion accompaniment. Any of the questions in this test could be expected to occur in a test on a folk-song from the British Isles and, indeed, Martin Codax's song is thought by some to be a very early example of written-down folk-song, since the style is unlike most of the surviving art music from this period.

Test 9: *Ma dame, trop vous mesprenés*

The origin of this three-voice *chanson* is, like much early music, not entirely certain. Though one manuscript gives no composer at all, it is known to come from the late 15th-century court of Charles the Bold (1433–1477), Duke of Burgundy, and may even be by the Duke himself. Burgundy was then not just a region of France, but an enormous union of territories that swept in a great arc from south-eastern France through Luxembourg, Belgium and into Holland—the most powerful political force in western Europe. Their wealth allowed the Dukes of Burgundy to patronize the arts on a magnificent scale, and their name is used to describe composers of the period as being of the Burgundian school.

The migration south of composers from northern France and the low countries, the former Burgundian lands, was crucial in the development of late-Renaissance polyphony in Italy. Although the rhythms and part-writing in this *chanson* are not so effortlessly flowing as those in late 16th-century music, many emergent features of the new style can be heard in the use of brief imitative points, treatment of dissonance and modern-sounding tonality. Two prominent elements that you would not expect to find in late-Renaissance music, however, are the frequent syncopations that allow individual parts to float free of a metrical pulse (for example, look at the last nine bars of the bass part) and the use of the 'Landini cadence'—the leading note dropping to the sixth before rising to the tonic (as in the soprano part of bar 7). This pattern is named after the late 14th-century composer, Francesco Landini, and was widely used by French and English composers of the early Renaissance.

The music on Track 8 is a strophic song from Galicia, a province in north-western Spain: the town of Vigo mentioned in the text is on the coast, close to the border with Portugal. The melody, the opening of which is given below, is repeated eleven times in the following pattern:

Intro	Intro	Verse 1	Verse 2	Interlude	Verse 3	Verse 4	Interlude	Verse 5	Verse 6	Coda

The words are in Galician, a language related to Portugese:

1. *Mandad' ei comigo ca ven meu amigo:*
   E irei, madr', a Vigo!

   My love's coming home, a message has come:
   Mother, I am going to Vigo!

2. *Comigu' ei mandado ca ven meu amado:*
   E irei, madr', a Vigo!

   He is due today, his message does say:
   Mother, I am going to Vigo!

3. *Ca ven meu amigo e ven san' e vivo:*
   E irei, madr', a Vigo!

   The message does tell that he's safe and well:
   Mother, I am going to Vigo!

4. *Ca ven meu amado e ven viv' e sano:*
   E irei, madr', a Vigo!

   My love's on his way, well and safe today:
   Mother, I am going to Vigo!

5. *Ca ven san' e vivo e d'el rei amigo:*
   E irei, madr', a Vigo!

   Safe and well, I can sing, and a friend of the king:
   Mother, I am going to Vigo!

6. *Ca ven viv' e sano e d'el rei privado:*
   E irei, madr', a Vigo!

   Well and safe he comes here, the king's favoured peer:
   Mother, I am going to Vigo!

The melody is in three phrases. The basic outline of the first two is:

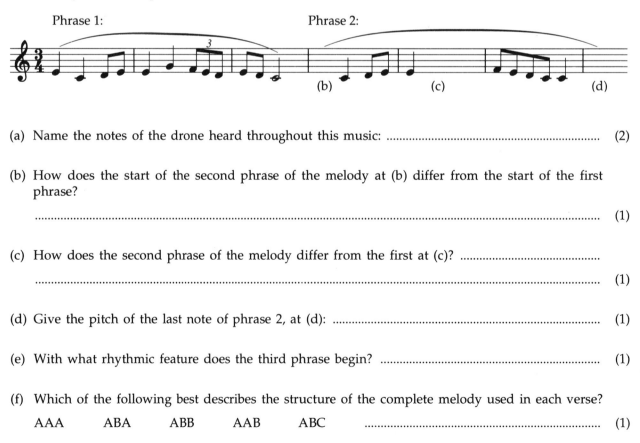

(a) Name the notes of the drone heard throughout this music: .... (2)

(b) How does the start of the second phrase of the melody at (b) differ from the start of the first phrase?

   .... (1)

(c) How does the second phrase of the melody differ from the first at (c)? ....

   .... (1)

(d) Give the pitch of the last note of phrase 2, at (d): .... (1)

(e) With what rhythmic feature does the third phrase begin? .... (1)

(f) Which of the following best describes the structure of the complete melody used in each verse?

   AAA   ABA   ABB   AAB   ABC   .... (1)

(g) What is the total range of the complete melody? .... (1)

(h) What type of voice sings the melody? .... (1)

(i) In which of the following modes is this music?

   major

   minor

   Dorian

   Mixolydian

   Aeolian   .... (2)

(j) (i) Briefly describe the predominant musical texture throughout most of this piece:

        .... (1)

    (ii) Apart from the drone, mention one of the ways in which this texture is sometimes varied:

        .... (1)

(k) Mention two ways in which the final section (labelled 'coda' on the diagram) differs from the first instrumental section:

    (i)   .... (1)

    (ii) .... (1)

Total: 15 marks

[15]

Here is the text of the *chanson* you will hear on this track:

Ma dame, trop vous mesprenés   My lady, you do great wrong
quant vers moy ne vous gouvernés.   by misbehaving towards me.
Aultrement qui l'oseroit dire?   Who would dare say otherwise?
Car oncque saint tant de martire   For no saint ever suffered such martyrdom
n'endura que vous me donés.   as you cause me.

The music below gives just one of the three vocal parts in each section of this *chanson*. The soprano is given for the first section, the tenor for the second, and the bass for the third:

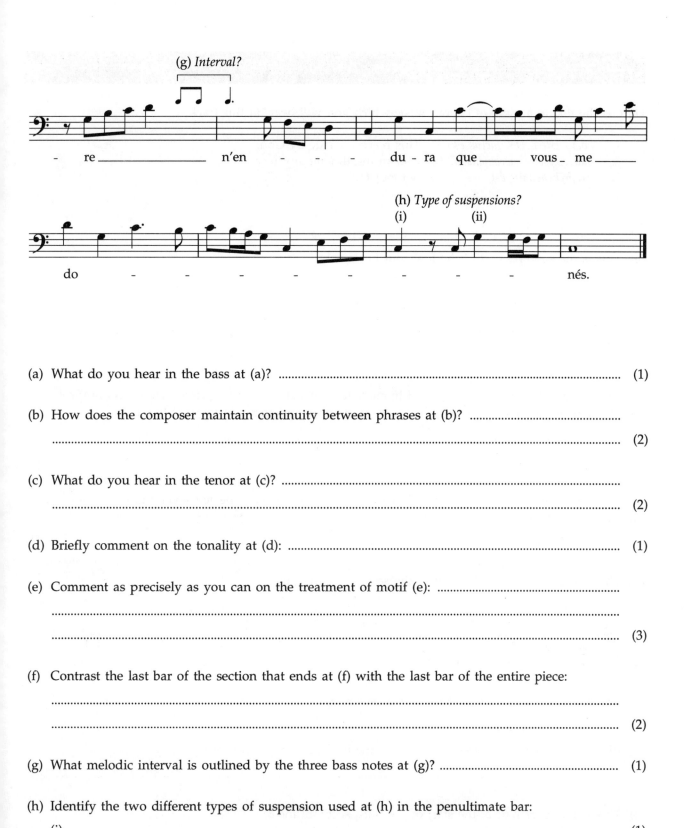

(a) What do you hear in the bass at (a)? .... (1)

(b) How does the composer maintain continuity between phrases at (b)? ....

.... (2)

(c) What do you hear in the tenor at (c)? ....

.... (2)

(d) Briefly comment on the tonality at (d): .... (1)

(e) Comment as precisely as you can on the treatment of motif (e): ....

....

.... (3)

(f) Contrast the last bar of the section that ends at (f) with the last bar of the entire piece:

....

.... (2)

(g) What melodic interval is outlined by the three bass notes at (g)? .... (1)

(h) Identify the two different types of suspension used at (h) in the penultimate bar:

(i)   .... (1)

(ii) .... (1)

Total: 14 marks

[17]

Here is the text of a piece of choral music which you will hear on this track:

1. *Locus iste a Deo factus est*   This place is made by God;
2. *inaestimabile sacramentum*   It is an inestimable mystery
3. *irreprehensibilis est.*   without fault.

(a) This is the soprano part of the first four bars:

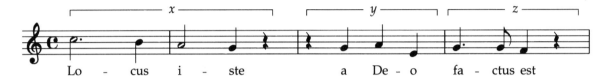

(i) A version of motif *x* is repeated immediately after the four bars printed above. As precisely as you can describe how it differs from the original version in the first two bars:

....

.... (3)

(ii) Which one of the three motifs shown in the music above is repeated several times in slightly varied forms?

.... (1)

(b) This is the bass part at the start of the second section (line 2):

(i) Describe the rest of the bass part in this section: ....

.... (2)

(ii) How does the soprano part relate to the bass part in this section? ....

.... (1)

(c) This is the tenor part at the start of the third section (line 3):

(i) Describe the continuation of this tenor part in the four bars following the music above:

.... (2)

(ii) How does the soprano part relate to the tenor part at the beginning of this section?

.... (2)

[18]

(d) Which of these words most accurately describes the form of the whole piece?

rondo

binary

ternary

variations

fugue .... (1)

(e) Which of these words most accurately describes the genre of the music?

madrigal

anthem

motet

mass

chorale .... (2)

(f) Which of these composers wrote this music?

Palestrina

Purcell

Handel

Haydn

Bruckner

Britten .... (1)

Total: 15 marks

Follow this skeleton score of the first violin part as you listen to the orchestral piece on this track. Note that the repeats of both parts are observed on this recording.

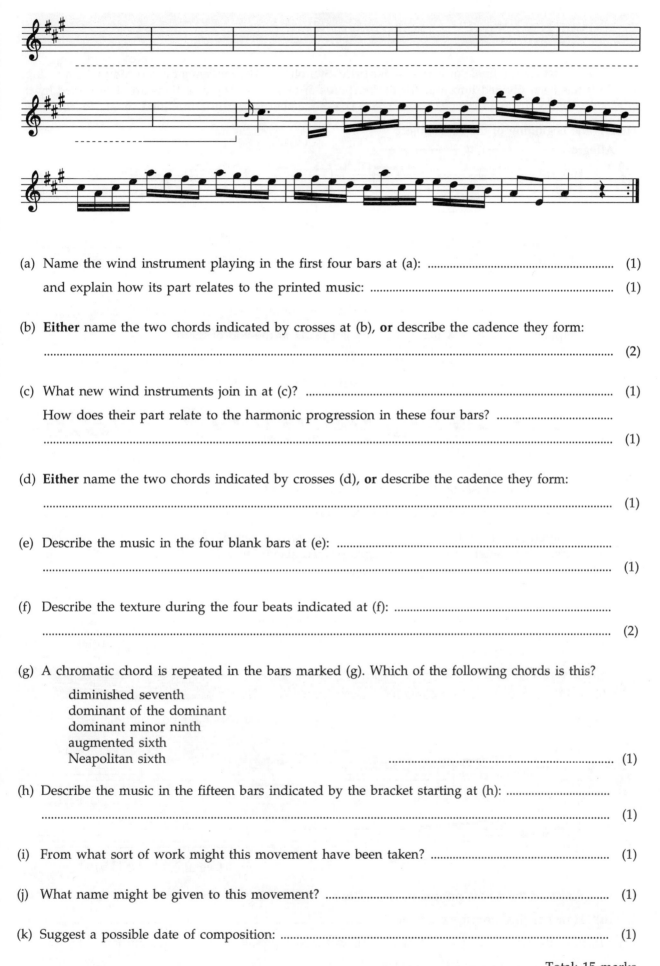

(a) Name the wind instrument playing in the first four bars at (a): .... (1)

and explain how its part relates to the printed music: .... (1)

(b) **Either** name the two chords indicated by crosses at (b), **or** describe the cadence they form:

.... (2)

(c) What new wind instruments join in at (c)? .... (1)

How does their part relate to the harmonic progression in these four bars? ....

.... (1)

(d) **Either** name the two chords indicated by crosses (d), **or** describe the cadence they form:

.... (1)

(e) Describe the music in the four blank bars at (e): ....

.... (1)

(f) Describe the texture during the four beats indicated at (f): ....

.... (2)

(g) A chromatic chord is repeated in the bars marked (g). Which of the following chords is this?

    diminished seventh
    dominant of the dominant
    dominant minor ninth
    augmented sixth
    Neapolitan sixth   .... (1)

(h) Describe the music in the fifteen bars indicated by the bracket starting at (h): ....

.... (1)

(i) From what sort of work might this movement have been taken? .... (1)

(j) What name might be given to this movement? .... (1)

(k) Suggest a possible date of composition: .... (1)

Total: 15 marks

Track 12 consists of the finale of Haydn's 'Surprise' Symphony. The movement is too complex for a single test so it has been divided into four for the purposes of this book. These sections are determined by the silences which occur at 1'01", 1'22" and 2'55". The movement is cast in a modified sonata form.

Here is the beginning of the first subject:

(a) How do the first eight bars above differ when they are repeated? .... (2)

(b) What happens in the bars which have been left blank at the end of the music above?

.... (2)

(c) After only a few more bars, the opening theme returns in a modified form:

   (i)   How is the anacrusis (at the question mark) changed? .... (1)

   (ii) What **new** instrument is added to those playing this melody? .... (1)

(d) The transition (a loud tutti) begins on the last note of this melody. Listen to the bass part and, using appropriate letters from both excerpts printed above (w, x, y, y^1, z) list four motifs in the order in which they are now used in the bass:

   (i)   ....   (ii)   ....   (iii)   ....   (iv)   .... (4)

(e) What sort of cadence do you hear at the very end of this section? .... (1)

Total: 11 marks

Here is the violin part of the second subject, in which a couple of bars have been left blank:

(h) *Bass and harmonic progression?*

Codetta (tutti for 13 bars)

(f) (i)   Which of the motifs printed in Test 12 is adapted to form the motif marked (f)? .... (1)

     (ii) How has this motif been adapted? .... (1)

(g) Which of the motifs printed in Test 12 is played repeatedly as an accompaniment figure by the

second violins in the second subject? .... (1)

[22]

(h) Describe the bass part and the harmonic progressions in the first eight bars of the second subject:

....

.... (5)

(i) The codetta, a loud tutti starting at the end of the second subject, uses some of the scale patterns of the transition. Identify the only three chords used in this section:

.... (3)

Total: 11 marks

Test 12b

The brief development leads back to the recapitulation in sections clearly defined by contrasting dynamics:

Development		Recapitulation			
(j) *soft*	(k) *loud*	(l) *soft*	(m) *loud*	(n) *soft*	(o) *loud*

(j) The first subject in the tonic, as printed at the top of the facing page, is heard in section (j).

   (i) Which combination of instruments plays the melody this time? .... (2)

   (ii) What happens instead of the printed repeat? .... (2)

(k) Briefly state how the string and wind parts differ from each other in the loud section (k):

.... (2)

(l) How does the key of the first subject at (l) relate to its key at (j)? .... (1)

(m) How does the key of the first subject at (m) relate to its key at (j)? .... (2)

Total: 9 marks

Test 12c

This final section starts with the recapitulation of the second subject (see printed music in Test 12a), after which the coda begins with this music:

(n) In the quieter wind passage which follows this music:

   (i) Which two motifs from the music printed in Test 12 (opposite) can you hear? .... (2)

   (ii) What is the harmonic function of the horns? .... (2)

(o) At the end of this quieter passage in G major, the timpanist heralds the final tutti with a bar of very loud semiquavers.

   (i) Comment on the tonality at this point: .... (2)

   (ii) Describe **two** ways in which the tonic key is emphasized in the final bars of the movement:

.... (2)

(p) The movement was described above as being 'cast in a modified sonata form'. In what way has sonata form been modified?

.... (2)

Total: 10 marks

The music on Track 13 is a recording of Satie's *Gymnopédie* No. 1, orchestrated by Debussy. The score below shows the original piano version. The questions opposite refer mainly to Debussy's orchestration of this music.

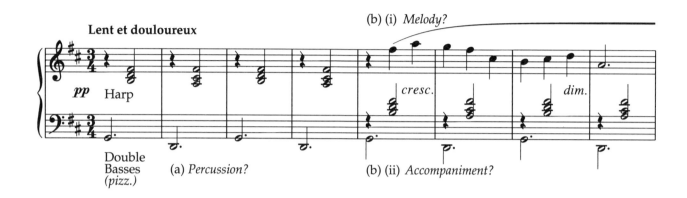

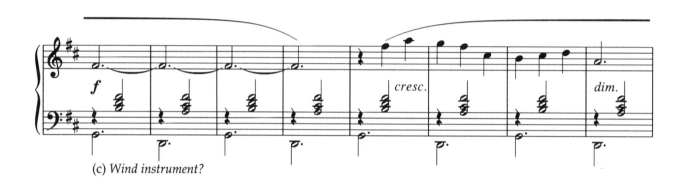

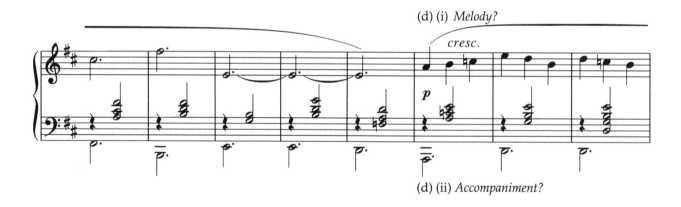

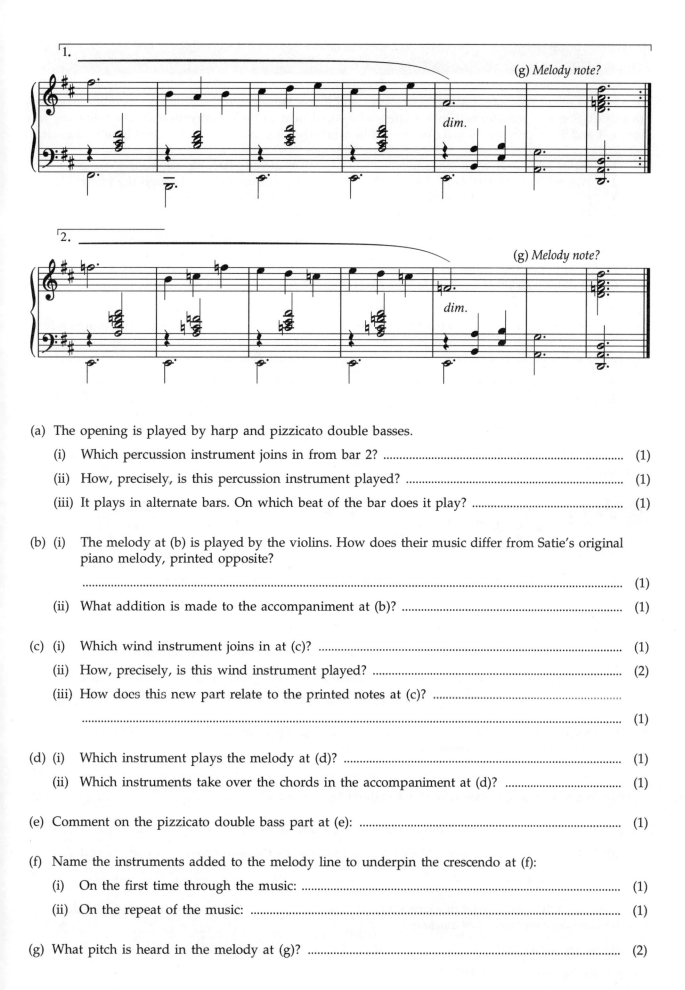

(a) The opening is played by harp and pizzicato double basses.

   (i) Which percussion instrument joins in from bar 2? .... (1)

   (ii) How, precisely, is this percussion instrument played? .... (1)

   (iii) It plays in alternate bars. On which beat of the bar does it play? .... (1)

(b) (i) The melody at (b) is played by the violins. How does their music differ from Satie's original piano melody, printed opposite?

      .... (1)

   (ii) What addition is made to the accompaniment at (b)? .... (1)

(c) (i) Which wind instrument joins in at (c)? .... (1)

   (ii) How, precisely, is this wind instrument played? .... (2)

   (iii) How does this new part relate to the printed notes at (c)? ....

      .... (1)

(d) (i) Which instrument plays the melody at (d)? .... (1)

   (ii) Which instruments take over the chords in the accompaniment at (d)? .... (1)

(e) Comment on the pizzicato double bass part at (e): .... (1)

(f) Name the instruments added to the melody line to underpin the crescendo at (f):

   (i) On the first time through the music: .... (1)

   (ii) On the repeat of the music: .... (1)

(g) What pitch is heard in the melody at (g)? .... (2)

Total: 16 marks

[25]

This Lied is about the Lorelei, a legendary lass who threw herself into the Rhine because her lover was unfaithful. She was transformed into a siren who lured men to their destruction. In the following text lines 1–4 and 9–8 represent the voice of the victim, while the alternate stanzas represent Lorelei, the witch.

1.	*'Es ist schon spät, es ist schon kalt,*	'It is already late, already cold
2.	*Was reit'st du einsam durch den Wald?*	Why ride you alone through the forest?
3.	*Der Wald ist lang, du bist allein,*	The forest is big, you are alone,
4.	*Du schöne Braut! ich führ' dich heim!'*	You beautiful bride! I will take you home!'
5.	*'Groß ist der Männer Trug und List,*	'Great is men's deceit and cunning
6.	*Vor Schmerz mein Herz gebrochen ist,*	With grief my heart is broken,
7.	*Wohl irrt das Waldhorn her und hin,*	The hunting horn sounds hither and thither
8.	*O flieh'! o flieh'! du weißt nicht, wer ich bin.'*	O fly! o fly! you know not who I am.'
9.	*'So reich geschmückt ist Roß und Weib,*	'So richly arrayed are horse and woman,
10.	*So wunderschön, so wunderschön der junge Leib;*	So breathtakingly beautiful your young body:
11.	*Jetzt kenn' ich dich, Got steh' mir bei!*	Now I know you, God stay by me!
12.	*Du bist die Hexe Loreley!'*	You are the witch, Lorelei.'
13.	*'Du kennst mich wohl, von hohem Stein*	'You know me well, from its high rock
14.	*Schaut still mein Schloß tief in den Rhein.*	My castle looks calmly deep into the Rhine.
15.	*Es ist schon spät, es ist schon kalt,*	It is already late, already cold,
16.	*Kommst nimmermehr aus diesem Wald.'*	You will nevermore leave this forest.'

The piano introduction begins with 'horn fifths', imitating the sound of the *Waldhörner* (hunting horns) mentioned in line 7 of the text:

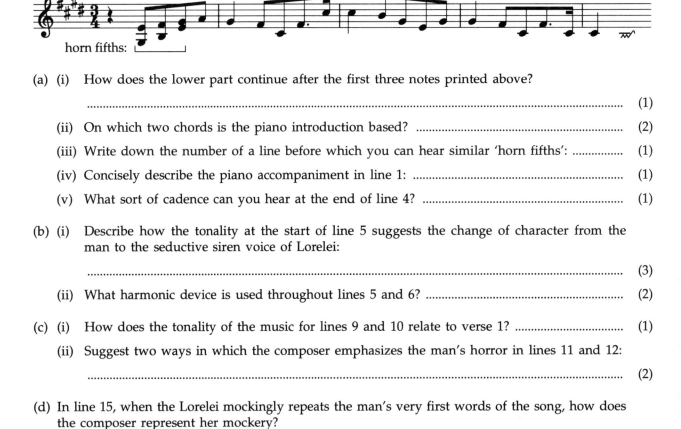

horn fifths:

(a) (i)   How does the lower part continue after the first three notes printed above?

    .... (1)

   (ii) On which two chords is the piano introduction based? .... (2)

   (iii) Write down the number of a line before which you can hear similar 'horn fifths': .... (1)

   (iv) Concisely describe the piano accompaniment in line 1: .... (1)

   (v) What sort of cadence can you hear at the end of line 4? .... (1)

(b) (i)   Describe how the tonality at the start of line 5 suggests the change of character from the man to the seductive siren voice of Lorelei:

    .... (3)

   (ii) What harmonic device is used throughout lines 5 and 6? .... (2)

(c) (i)   How does the tonality of the music for lines 9 and 10 relate to verse 1? .... (1)

   (ii) Suggest two ways in which the composer emphasizes the man's horror in lines 11 and 12:

    .... (2)

(d) In line 15, when the Lorelei mockingly repeats the man's very first words of the song, how does the composer represent her mockery?

   (i)   in the vocal line? ....

   (ii) in the piano harmonies? .... (2)

Total: 16 marks

Listen to the piece of dance music for piano on this track.

(a) Here is the melody of the first half of the opening eight-bar phrase:

    (i)   What sort of ornament can you hear at the beginning of this phrase? .... (1)

    (ii) What else does the pianist play with his right hand in these four bars? ....

        .... (2)

    (iii) Comment on the pianist's rhythmic interpretation of bars 3 and 4: ....

        .... (2)

    (iv) What are the only two chords used in the complete eight-bar phrase? .... (2)

(b) The first part of this piece consists of four eight-bar phrases which can be represented by letters, thus:

    A A^1 A A^2

    (i)   What do all these four phrases have in common? .... (1)

    (ii) In general terms, state how the harmony and tonality of both phrase A^1 and phrase A^2 differ from the original phrase A:

        Harmony: ....

        Tonality: .... (2)

(c) Here is an incomplete score of the new four-bar phrase which is heard immediately after phrase A^2:

    (i)   In the slightly modified repeat of this four-bar phrase, describe as precisely as you can how the harmonic progression relates to the harmonies outlined above:

        .... (2)

    (ii) What chord do you hear in the bar before the final perfect cadence? .... (1)

(d) (i)   Describe, in one word if possible, the performer's rhythmic interpretation throughout the whole piece:

        .... (1)

    (ii) What sort of dance is this? .... (1)

    (iii) Suggest the name of the composer of this music: .... (1)

        and the date of its composition: .... (1)

Total: 17 marks

On Track 16 there are two related movements for piano by Shostakovich. Listen to the first of these as you follow the skeleton score below and answer questions (a) to (i).

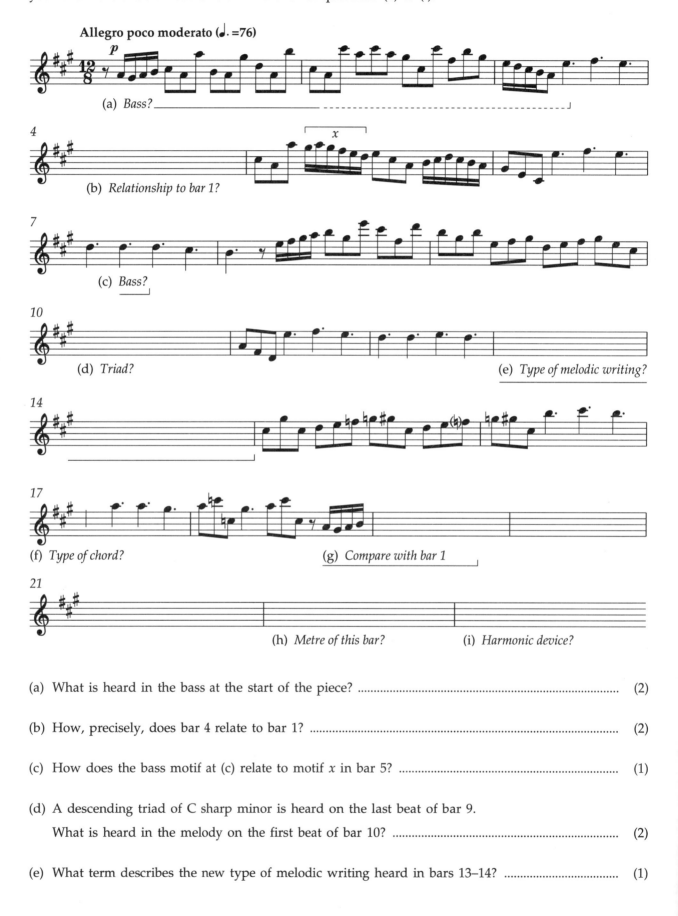

(a) What is heard in the bass at the start of the piece? .... (2)

(b) How, precisely, does bar 4 relate to bar 1? .... (2)

(c) How does the bass motif at (c) relate to motif *x* in bar 5? .... (1)

(d) A descending triad of C sharp minor is heard on the last beat of bar 9.

What is heard in the melody on the first beat of bar 10? .... (2)

(e) What term describes the new type of melodic writing heard in bars 13–14? .... (1)

(f) Which of the following types of chord is heard on the first beat of bar 17:

diminished triad, diminished seventh, dominant seventh, augmented sixth, Neapolitan sixth?

.... (1)

(g) Compare the bracketed passage at (g) with the motif in bar 1: ....

.... (1)

(h) In what metre is bar 22? .... (1)

(i) What harmonic device is heard from bar 23 to the end of the movement? ....

.... (3)

Total: 14 marks

Test 16a

Listen immediately to the second of the two recordings on Track 16 and answer questions (j) to (q) below:

(j) Compare this movement with the first in terms of:

(i) Key: .... (ii) Metre: .... (2)

(iii) Texture: .... (1)

(k) The first four bars consist of an unaccompanied melody.
Comment briefly on the construction of this melody: .... (2)

(l) Shortly after the start you will hear the opening four bars return an octave lower. Comment briefly on the harmonic pace from the start to the end of these four bars:

.... (1)

(m) The first half of this movement is purely diatonic. Which of the following does the composer then use for the first change of key?

a modulation to the dominant
a modulation to the subdominant
a modulation to the tonic minor
a tertiary modulation
an enharmonic modulation .... (1)

(n) Describe the pattern of key changes immediately following this modulation: ....

.... (1)

(o) What harmonic device is then used to re-establish the tonic key? .... (2)

(p) Name two of the compositional devices that are used to present the opening theme in new ways during the final section of the piece:

(i) .... (ii) .... (2)

(q) What type of composition is this? .... (1)

Total: 13 marks

[29]

The strophic song on Track 17 consists of four verses and choruses, interspersed with 'instrumental interludes', in the following pattern:

Intro	Verse 1	Chorus	Interlude	Verse 2	Chorus	Interlude	Verse 3	Chorus	Interlude	Verse 4	Chorus (twice)

The words of the verses and choruses are as follows (lines are numbered for your reference):

Verse 1
1. Have you heard of Phil the Fluter, from the town of Ballymuck?
2. The times were going hard on him, in fact, the man was bruk',
3. So he just sent out a notice to his neighbours, one and all,
4. As to how he'd like their company that ev'ning at the ball.
5. And when writin' out he was careful to suggest to them
6. That if they found a hat of his convenient to the door,
7. The more they put in, whenever he requested them,
8. 'The better would the music be for battherin' the floor'.

Chorus
9. With the toot o' the flute, and the twiddle o' the fiddle. Oh,
10. Hopping in the middle, like a herrin' on the griddle. Oh,
11. Up, down, hands a-rown' Crossin' to the wall,
12. Oh! hadn't we the gaiety at Phil the Fluter's Ball!

Verse 2
1. There was Misther Denis Dogherty, who kep' 'The Runnin' Dog';
2. There was little crooked Paddy from the Tiraloughett bog:
3. There were boys from ev'ry Barony, and girls from ev'ry 'art',
4. And the beautiful Miss Bradys, in their private ass an' cart,
5. Along with them came bouncing Mrs Cafferty,
6. Little Micky Mulligan was also to the fore;
7. Rose, Suzanne, and Margaret O'Rafferty.
8. The flow'r of Ardmagullion, and the Pride of Pethravore.

Chorus
9. With the toot o' the flute, ...

Verse 3
1. First little Micky Mulligan got up to show them how,
2. And then the widda' Cafferty steps out and makes her bow.
3. 'I could dance you off your legs', sez she, 'as sure as you are born,
4. If ye'll only make the piper play "The Hare Was In The Corn".'
5. So, Phil plays up to the best of his ability,
6. The lady and the gentleman begin to do their share;
7. 'Faith, then Mick, 'tis you that has agility!'
8. 'Begorra! Mrs Cafferty, yer leppin' like a hare!'

Chorus
9. With the toot o' the flute, ...

Verse 4
1. Then Phil the Fluter tipped a wink to little crooked Pat,
2. 'I think it's nearly time', sez he, 'for passin' round the hat'.
3. So Paddy passed the caubeen round, and looking mighty cute,
4. Sez, 'Ye've got to pay the piper when he toothers on the flute'.
5. Then all joined in wid the greatest joviality,
6. Covering the buckle and the shuffle, and the cut;
7. Jigs were danced, of the very finest quality,
8. But the Widda' beat the company at 'handeling the foot'.

Chorus
9. With the toot o' the flute, ...   *(repeated)*

Introduction and Interludes

(a) From which two lines of the song are the interludes and introduction taken?

.... (2)

(b) On what type of chord does the pianist pause immediately before the start of each verse?

.... (2)

Verses

(c) The first three lines of each verse feature a prominent rising interval in the vocal part.

What is this interval? .... (1)

(d) Compare the cadences at the ends of lines 2 and 4 of each verse: ....

.... (2)

(e) Give the number of a line in each verse where the music passes briefly through:

(i) The relative minor key: .... (1)

(ii) The dominant key: .... (1)

(f) State briefly how the pianist varies the accompaniment in verses 2, 3 and 4:

.... (2)

Choruses

(g) From which four lines of the verse is the melody of the chorus taken? .... (1)

(h) What new rhythm is briefly introduced by the pianist in the middle of the chorus? .... (1)

(i) Mention two other ways in which the accompaniment of the chorus differs from the accompaniment of the verses:

(i) .... (1)

(ii) .... (1)

(j) The final chorus is repeated at a faster tempo. The singer embellishes the final cadence of this repeat with a pause on a high note.

On what note of the scale does the singer pause? .... (1)

Total: 16 marks

The composer of this song, Percy French (1854–1920), was an Irish singer, songwriter, artist and professional entertainer, best remembered for this song and his ubiquitous epic, *Abdullah Bulbul Ameer*. He was also an early advocate of minstrel songs and banjo music (see *Aural Matters*, page 73), introducing both into his touring shows. Many of his songs draw on elements of Irish folk music and the Irish brogue, but all are essentially in the tradition of 19th-century music-hall song and parlour ballad (see *Aural Matters*, page 86).

The extract on Track 18 is taken from a piano concerto. Much of the thematic material is derived from this folk-song:

Listen to the opening 54 seconds as you follow the outline score below, and answer questions (a) to (i):

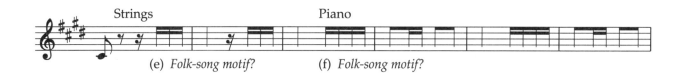

(a) Which of the motifs in the folk-song (*x, y* or *z*) is used at (a)? .... (1)

(b) What type of chords does the piano play at (b)? .... (2)

(c) What type of scale does the piano play at (c)? .... (2)

(d) How do the twelve bars of music at (d) relate to the first twelve bars of the extract?

.... (2)

(e) Which of the motifs in the folk-song (*x, y* or *z*) is used at (e)? .... (1)

(f) (i)   Which of the motifs in the folk-song (*x, y* or *z*) is used at (f)? .... (1)

    (ii) What technique is used to transform the opening of this motif?................................. (1)

(g) As precisely as you can, describe the instrumentation of the theme at (g): ....

.... (3)

(h) The first of the bracketed cadences at (h) is a perfect cadence, in the key of E.

    Compare the second cadence in terms of its type: .... and key: .... (2)

(i) How does the piano part relate to the printed music at (i)? .... (1)

Total: 16

Listen to the rest of Track 18 and answer questions (j) to (m). After further development of the material outlined above there is a cadenza in three sections, followed by a coda:

Cadenza			Coda
Cascading chords and arpeggios	Tranquil section	Gradually more animated	(Allegro ... con fuoco)

(j) The tranquil middle section of the cadenza is ten bars long, beginning with this motif:

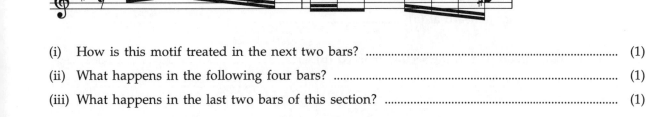

    (i)   How is this motif treated in the next two bars? .... (1)

    (ii) What happens in the following four bars? .... (1)

    (iii) What happens in the last two bars of this section? .... (1)

(k) From what previous material is the start of the coda derived? .... (1)

(l) The music before the cadenza is in C sharp minor. In what key does the coda end? .... (1)

(m) Suggest the composer: .... and date of composition of this concerto: .... (2)

Total: 7

Here is the text of the Latin motet on this track, together with an English translation for your information:

O salutaris hostia,   O sacrificial victim who brings salvation,
Quae caeli pandis ostium,   And opens wide the gates of heaven for us,
Bella premunt hostilia,   Battles and enemy attacks press us hard,
Da robur fer auxilium.   But you give strength and bring us help.

Here is the opening of the uppermost part, in which certain passages have been left blank:

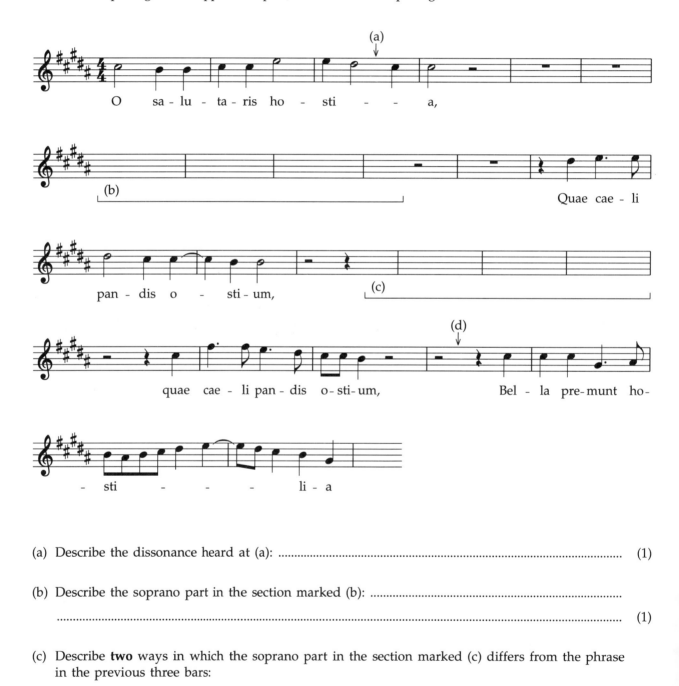

(a) Describe the dissonance heard at (a): .... (1)

(b) Describe the soprano part in the section marked (b): ....

.... (1)

(c) Describe **two** ways in which the soprano part in the section marked (c) differs from the phrase in the previous three bars:

....

.... (2)

(d) Describe the dissonance heard in the lower voices at (d): ....

.... (2)

[34]

(e) Upon which of the following is this music based?

harmonic minor scale

melodic minor scale

major scale

Dorian mode

Phrygian mode

Mixolydian mode .... (1)

(f) Listen to the very last repetition of the words *Da robur fer auxilium* in the soprano.

(i) Which **two** degrees of the scale have been chromatically altered in this phrase?

.... (2)

(ii) In what ways have these two degrees been altered?

....

.... (2)

(g) Describe, as precisely as you can, each of the five types of voice singing in this motet:

....

....

....

....

.... (5)

(h) Which **two** of the following terms most accurately describe the texture of the whole motet?

polychoral

polyphonic

fugal

canonic

imitative

homophonic

monophonic .... (2)

Total: 18 marks

The recording on this track is a setting by Schubert of an Italian text by the great 18th-century librettist, Metastasio. Repeats in the text are printed in full for clarity:

Da quel sembiante appresi	By that countenance I learned
a sospirand' amore,	to sigh with love,
a sospirand' amore,	
<u>*Sempre per quel sembiante*</u>	Ever for that countenance
<u>*sospirerò d'amore,*</u>	will I sigh with love.
Sempre per quel sembiante	
sospirerò d'amore.	
La face a cui m'accesi	The flame from which I caught my fire
solo m'alleta e piace,	alone entices me and delights,
solo m'alleta e piace,	
È fredda ogn'altra face	Too cold all other flames
per riscaldarmi il cuore,	to warm my heart.
È fredda ogn'altra face	
per riscaldarmi il cuore.	

Here is the bass of the piano introduction, followed by the first four bars of the vocal melody:

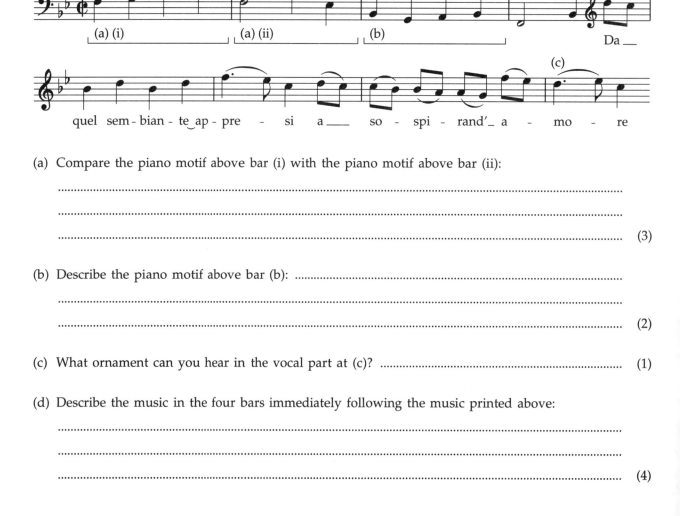

(a) Compare the piano motif above bar (i) with the piano motif above bar (ii):

....

....

.... (3)

(b) Describe the piano motif above bar (b): ....

....

.... (2)

(c) What ornament can you hear in the vocal part at (c)? .... (1)

(d) Describe the music in the four bars immediately following the music printed above:

....

....

.... (4)

(e) Here is the melody of the next section (the words underlined in the text opposite):

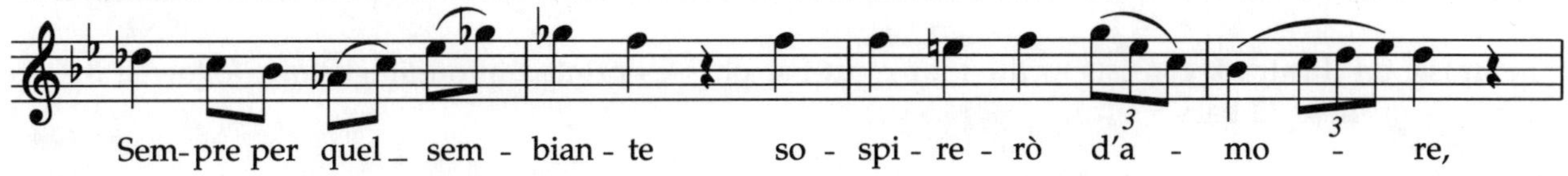

Sem-pre per quel _ sem - bian - te   so - spi - re - rò d'a - mo - re,

How is this melody changed when the same words are repeated in the following four bars?

....

....

.... (4)

(f) Which of the following best describes the whole song?

    da capo aria

    strophic song

    through-composed song

    Lied

    ballad

    mélodie   .... (1)

Total: 15 marks

[37]

The music on this track consists of the four eight-bar phrases printed in outline below, followed by two varations of these 32 bars.

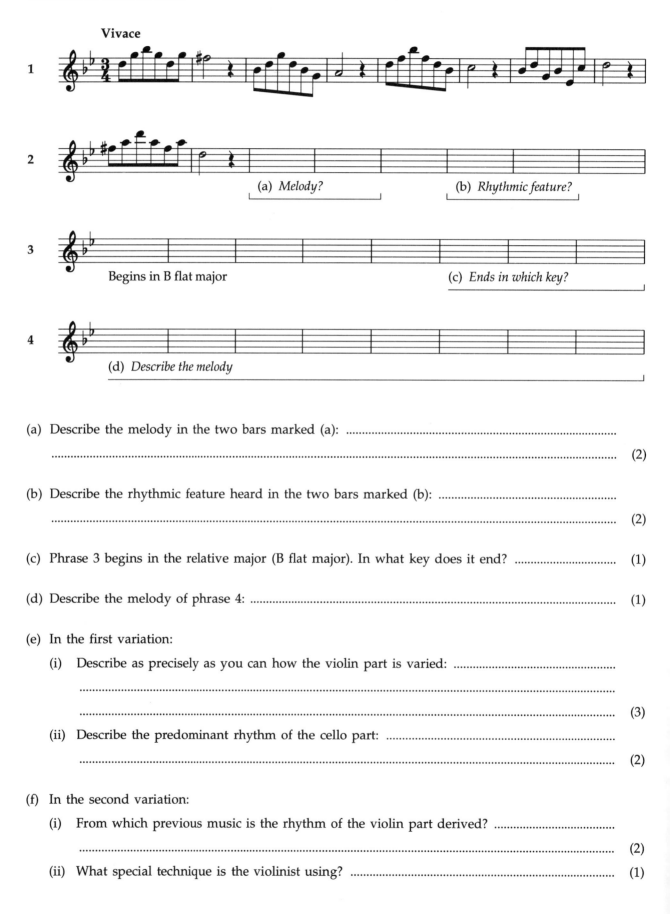

(a) Describe the melody in the two bars marked (a): ....

.... (2)

(b) Describe the rhythmic feature heard in the two bars marked (b): ....

.... (2)

(c) Phrase 3 begins in the relative major (B flat major). In what key does it end? .... (1)

(d) Describe the melody of phrase 4: .... (1)

(e) In the first variation:

   (i)   Describe as precisely as you can how the violin part is varied: ....

         ....

         .... (3)

   (ii) Describe the predominant rhythm of the cello part: ....

         .... (2)

(f) In the second variation:

   (i)   From which previous music is the rhythm of the violin part derived? ....

         .... (2)

   (ii) What special technique is the violinist using? .... (1)

(g) Apart from speed and instrumentation, what single element is common to the theme and the two variations?

.... (2)

(h) What other instrument, apart from violin and cello, can you hear? .... (1)

(i) Which of these best describes the type of work from which this movement is taken?

    concerto grosso

    trio sonata

    solo sonata

    canzona

    ricercare   .... (1)

(j) Suggest the name of a possible composer of this music: .... (1)

and the date of its composition: .... (1)

Total: 20 marks

Listen to the first 65 seconds from the piece of chamber music on this track. The opening of the clarinet part is printed below and the plan then represents the remaining three lines of music. All repeats are observed on the recording:

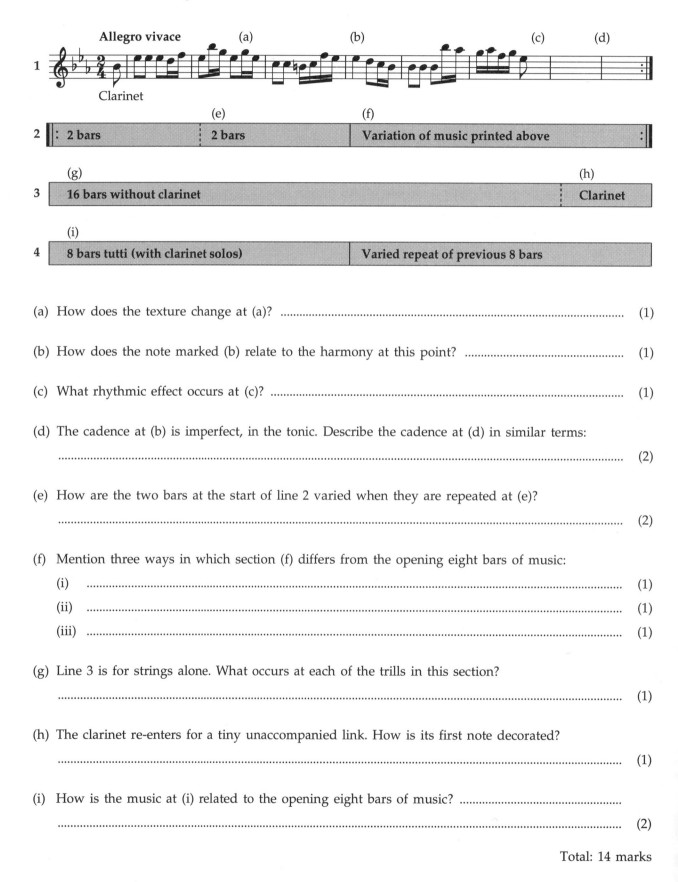

(a) How does the texture change at (a)? .... (1)

(b) How does the note marked (b) relate to the harmony at this point? .... (1)

(c) What rhythmic effect occurs at (c)? .... (1)

(d) The cadence at (b) is imperfect, in the tonic. Describe the cadence at (d) in similar terms:

.... (2)

(e) How are the two bars at the start of line 2 varied when they are repeated at (e)?

.... (2)

(f) Mention three ways in which section (f) differs from the opening eight bars of music:

   (i) .... (1)

   (ii) .... (1)

   (iii) .... (1)

(g) Line 3 is for strings alone. What occurs at each of the trills in this section?

.... (1)

(h) The clarinet re-enters for a tiny unaccompanied link. How is its first note decorated?

.... (1)

(i) How is the music at (i) related to the opening eight bars of music? ....

.... (2)

Total: 14 marks

Now listen to the rest of the movement, and answer the questions (j) to (q) below:

(j)   After the sections referenced above, there is an extended passage for clarinet, accompanied by strings. What are the two most prominent features of the clarinet writing in this section?

   (i)   .... (1)

   (ii) .... (1)

(k)   There are four bars for strings alone and then the elaborate clarinet writing resumes. Describe the function of the cello part throughout all of this music:

   .... (1)

(l)   Lines 1 and 2 of the music opposite then return, without repeats and with one other change. Where does this other change occur?

   .... (1)

(m) The next passage is for strings alone, and is played slightly slower in this performance.

   Describe the tonality of this passage: .... (1)

The music slows to a pause, after which the clarinet joins in again for eight bars. A softer section then begins with the following clarinet theme:

(n) (i)   Which two bars are varied by the clarinet on the repeat of this theme? .... (1)

   (ii) Describe, as precisely as possible, the part played by the cello throughout this section:

      ....

      .... (3)

(o) (i)   How is motif (o) treated in the next section? ....

      .... (3)

   (ii) What pattern is outlined by the cello in this section? .... (1)

(p)   On what note of the scale does the clarinet end the movement? .... (1)

(q) (i)   From what type of work is this movement taken? ....

   (ii) Which movement in that work do you believe this to be? ....

   (iii) In what form is this movement? ....

   (iv) Suggest a date when you believe the work was written: .... (4)

Total: 18 marks

Listen to the first section of the music on this track, ending with the silence at 1' 17". Follow the outline score below and answer questions (a) to (e). The piece is composed in mainly eight-bar phrases, each with a varied repeat. Most of the questions concern the ways in which these repeats are varied.

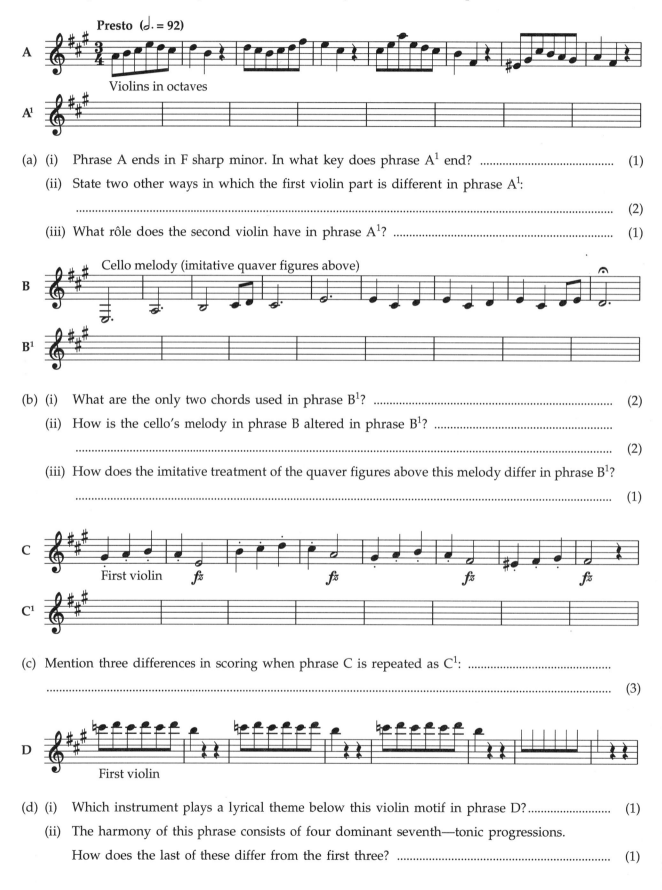

(a) (i)   Phrase A ends in F sharp minor. In what key does phrase A^1 end? .... (1)

    (ii) State two other ways in which the first violin part is different in phrase A^1:

    .... (2)

    (iii) What rôle does the second violin have in phrase A^1? .... (1)

(b) (i)   What are the only two chords used in phrase B^1? .... (2)

    (ii) How is the cello's melody in phrase B altered in phrase B^1? ....

    .... (2)

    (iii) How does the imitative treatment of the quaver figures above this melody differ in phrase B^1?

    .... (1)

(c) Mention three differences in scoring when phrase C is repeated as C^1: ....

.... (3)

(d) (i)   Which instrument plays a lyrical theme below this violin motif in phrase D? .... (1)

    (ii) The harmony of this phrase consists of four dominant seventh—tonic progressions.

    How does the last of these differ from the first three? .... (1)

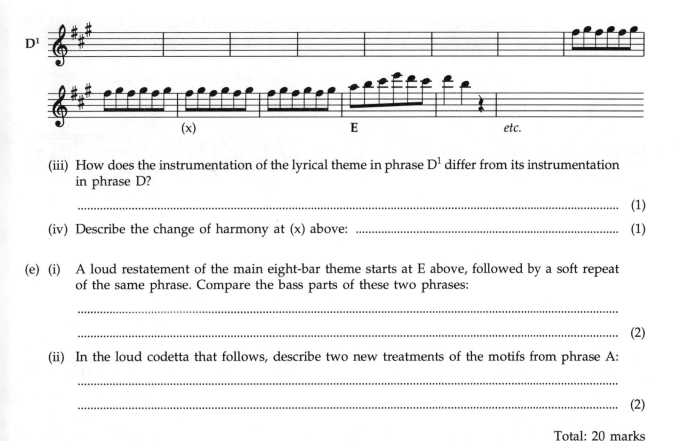

D¹   (x)   E   *etc.*

(iii) How does the instrumentation of the lyrical theme in phrase D¹ differ from its instrumentation in phrase D?

.... (1)

(iv) Describe the change of harmony at (x) above: .... (1)

(e) (i) A loud restatement of the main eight-bar theme starts at E above, followed by a soft repeat of the same phrase. Compare the bass parts of these two phrases:

....

.... (2)

(ii) In the loud codetta that follows, describe two new treatments of the motifs from phrase A:

....

.... (2)

Total: 20 marks

─────────────────────────── *Test 23a* ───────────────────────────

You have probably realized by now that this movement is a scherzo. It follows the usual pattern of scherzo–trio–scherzo, and in Test 23 you heard the first of these sections. Now listen to the trio and answer the questions below (the repeat of the scherzo after the trio is identical to its first appearance—sit back and enjoy it without having to worry about further questions!). The trio begins with this phrase:

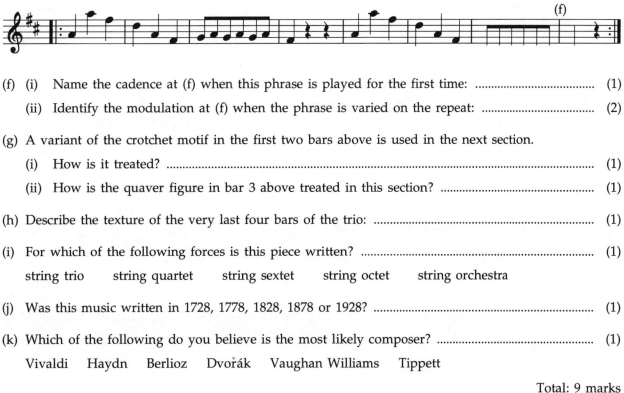

(f) (i) Name the cadence at (f) when this phrase is played for the first time: .... (1)

(ii) Identify the modulation at (f) when the phrase is varied on the repeat: .... (2)

(g) A variant of the crotchet motif in the first two bars above is used in the next section.

(i) How is it treated? .... (1)

(ii) How is the quaver figure in bar 3 above treated in this section? .... (1)

(h) Describe the texture of the very last four bars of the trio: .... (1)

(i) For which of the following forces is this piece written? .... (1)

string trio   string quartet   string sextet   string octet   string orchestra

(j) Was this music written in 1728, 1778, 1828, 1878 or 1928? .... (1)

(k) Which of the following do you believe is the most likely composer? .... (1)

Vivaldi   Haydn   Berlioz   Dvořák   Vaughan Williams   Tippett

Total: 9 marks

You will hear a complete movement for string quartet. The first violin part begins as follows:

(a) (i)   What does the second violin play during these four bars?

.... (2)

(ii) Why does this opening music sound as though it is in $\frac{9}{8}$ metre?

....

.... (2)

(b) The first subject consists of six statements of the phrase printed above in various versions, starting as follows:

Bars 1–4	5–8	9–12	13–16	17–20	21–24
A	A¹	A²			

(i)   How does phrase A¹ differ from phrase A? .... (1)

(ii) In what key is phrase A²? .... (1)

(iii) Complete the three empty boxes above to show the phrase structure of bars 13–24.   (3)

(c) State two ways in which the cello part differs from the other string parts in the first subject:

(i)   .... (1)

(ii) .... (1)

There is then a four-bar transition ...

... leading to the second subject:

(d) (i)   What is unusual about the harmonization of this second subject? ....

.... (1)

(ii) How does the composer maintain a sense of momentum during this more lyrical theme?

.... (1)

(e) After some further sixteen bars, the second subject reaches a climax. Mention three techniques that the composer uses to achieve this climax:

(i) .... (1)

(ii) .... (1)

(iii) .... (1)

Immediately after the climax, the following passage is heard:

(f) Comment on the instrumentation of the music printed above: ....

.... (1)

(g) After six more bars you will hear a short passage for viola and cello in octaves, leading into the next section of the form.

(i) What is this next section? .... (1)

(ii) Consider your answer to (i) above, and then identify the musical form of this movement as

precisely as possible: .... (2)

(h) Mention two ways in which the coda differs from the rest of the movement:

(i) .... (1)

(ii) .... (1)

(i) (i) Which movement of the quartet does this music form? .... (1)

(ii) Suggest the name of the composer of this movement: .... (1)

Total: 24 marks

[45]

Here are the words of the complete song on this track, followed by the music of the first verse:

Verse 1
1. Come you, Mary, there's a dear!
2. Mind no more the plaguy dairy!
3. Milk can never match your white.
4.   Come you, Mary!

Verse 2
1. All the music of my scythe
2. Sang you in the heated meadow;
3. And I turned for you, when fell
4.   Every shadow!

Verse 3
1. Down with pails, and bring those lips
2. (Rose-leaves in the happy dairy)
3. To the chestnut where we kiss.
4.   Come you, Mary!

(a) Name the pitch of the note sung at (a): .... (1)

(b) Describe the rhythm sung to the word 'never' at (b): .... (1)

(c) Which previous bar of the vocal part is adapted to form the singer's melody at (c)? .... (1)

(d) Line 4 of each verse has only four syllables. How does the composer maintain a sense of regular two-bar phrasing at this point?

.... (1)

(e) (i) How does the figuration of the piano accompaniment differ in verse 2? ....

.... (1)

    (ii) How else, apart from figuration, is the short piano introduction to verse 2 different from that before verses 1 and 3?

.... (1)

(f) How is the melody at the end of verse 2 changed to reflect the words 'when fell every shadow'?

.... (2)

(g) Write down a word from either verse 2 or verse 3 where the vocal writing is not entirely syllabic:

.... (1)

(h) What change is made to the vocal line to produce a climax at the end of the last verse?

.... (2)

(i) What type of voice is singing this song? .... (2)

(j) Suggest a date when you believe this song was written: .... (1)

Total: 14 marks

[47]

Study the chorale melody printed below and then listen to Track 26. The composition you will hear is based on this melody and is played on the piano.

(a) Comment on the ways in which this chorale melody is used in the music that you hear:

....

....

.... (3)

(b) What change occurs in the treatment of the last line of the chorale (bracketed in the music above) when it is heard for the final time?

....

.... (1)

(c) Name the harmonic device heard in the music after the chorale has ended:

.... (2)

(d) Comment on the rhythm of (i) the treble part, and (ii) the bass part, in relation to the chorale melody printed above:

    (i)   Treble: .... (2)

    (ii) Bass: .... (2)

(e) What type of piece is this? .... (2)

(f) The music on this track is a transcription for piano of a composition by an earlier composer.

    (i)   Suggest the name of the original composer: .... (1)

    (ii) Give **two** reasons for this suggestion: ....

        ....

        .... (2)

    (iii) Suggest the name of the composer who made this transcription: .... (1)

Total: 16 marks

[48]

Here is the Latin text of the vocal music on this track, with an English translation for your information:

1. *Deus in adiutorium meum intende*   O God reach forth to my aid
2. *Domine ad adiuvandum me festina.*   O Lord make haste to help me.
3. *Gloria Patri et Filio et Spiritui Sancto.*   Glory be to the Father and to the Son and to the Holy Spirit.
4. *Sicut erat in principio, et nunc, et semper,*   As it was in the beginning, is now, and ever shall be,
5. *Et in saecula saeculorum. Amen.*   World without end. Amen.
6. *Alleluia, alleluia, alleluia, alleluia.*

(a) In line 1, which one of the following terms best describes the opening solo?

    antiphon

    plainsong

    idée fixe

    leitmotif

    monotone

    heterophony   .... (1)

(b) Here is an outline of the melody at the start of line 2:

Do – mi – ne ad ad - iu - van - dum me fe - sti - - na,

(b) *Type of chord and texture?*   (c) *Harmonies?*

  (i) Describe the one type of chord used throughout the passage marked (b):

    .... (2)

  (ii) Describe the texture in this same passage as fully as you can:

    ....

    .... (2)

(c) Describe the harmonies at (c) in the above music as fully as you can:

    ....

    ....

    .... (3)

(d) (i) What is the single most important rhythmic change which occurs in line 3 of the text?

    .... (1)

  (ii) Describe the texture in the setting of line 3: .... (1)

(e) Describe the texture in the setting of line 6: .... (2)

Total: 12 marks

Here is the opening melody of an organ piece, the first half of which can be heard on this track:

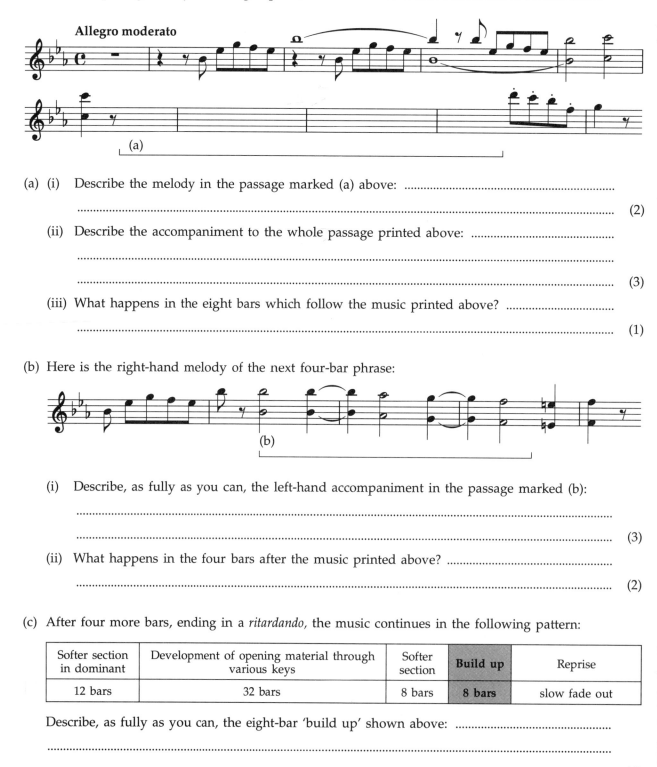

(a) (i) Describe the melody in the passage marked (a) above: ....

.... (2)

(ii) Describe the accompaniment to the whole passage printed above: ....

....

.... (3)

(iii) What happens in the eight bars which follow the music printed above? ....

.... (1)

(b) Here is the right-hand melody of the next four-bar phrase:

(i) Describe, as fully as you can, the left-hand accompaniment in the passage marked (b):

....

.... (3)

(ii) What happens in the four bars after the music printed above? ....

.... (2)

(c) After four more bars, ending in a *ritardando*, the music continues in the following pattern:

Softer section in dominant	Development of opening material through various keys	Softer section	Build up	Reprise
12 bars	32 bars	8 bars	8 bars	slow fade out

Describe, as fully as you can, the eight-bar 'build up' shown above: ....

....

.... (4)

(d) Which of the following best describes this type of organ music?

French Classical   German Baroque   Spanish Baroque
French Romantic   German neo-classical   20th century   .... (1)

Total: 16 marks

Use the table below to record your progress while working through this book:

Name:					Test	Date	Mark	Out of
Test	**Date**	**Mark**	**Out of**		**Test**	**Date**	**Mark**	**Out of**
1			15		15			17
2			15		16			14
3			14		16a			13
4			15		17			16
5			20		18			16
6			14		18a			7
6a			10		19			18
7			10		20			15
8			15		21			20
9			14		22			14
10			15		22a			18
11			15		23			20
12			11		23a			9
12a			11		24			24
12b			9		25			14
12c			10		26			16
13			16		27			12
14			16		28			16

A Scheme of Work and Answers

If this book is being used primarily for examination practice towards the end of a course, when students have already learnt to recognize a wide variety of techniques and styles, a random presentation of tests (possibly in the published order) may be desirable. An alternative approach is suggested below, suitable for use with students who are working through *Aural Matters*, in order, on their own. It shows how many of the extracts in that book can be followed up with a test from this volume, enabling teachers to check the understanding of forms and styles—both in the context of similar music and through the exploration of comparisons with related music by different composers or from different periods.

Aural Matters		*Aural Matters In Practice*	
Test 38	Elaboration of a monophonic folk tune		
	compared with monophonic medieval music	Test 8	(Codax)
Test 46	Folk-song of the industrial period		
	compared with 19th-century popular song	Test 17	(French)
Test 74	Renaissance motet (Victoria)	Test 7	(Sheppard) and Test 19 (Tallis)
	compared with Romantic motet	Test 10	(Bruckner)
	compared with Anglican church music	Test 6	(Stanford)
	compared with medieval polyphony	Test 9	(Charles the Bold)
Test 78	Baroque polychoral music (Gabrieli)	Test 27	(Padilla)
Test 79	Fugue (Bach) compared with modern fugue	Test 16	(Shostakovich)
	compared with Romantic organ music	Test 28	(Lefébure-Wély)
Test 80	Trio sonata (Corelli)		
	compared with solo sonata	Test 21	(Corelli)
	compared with Romantic chamber music	Test 23	(Dvořák) and Test 24 (Mendelssohn)
Test 81	*Style galant* (Martini)	Test 5	(Dibdin)
Test 82	Baroque concerto (Vivaldi)	Test 1	(Matteis)
	compared with Romantic concerto	Test 18	(Rimsky-Korsakov)
Test 83	Ground bass aria (Purcell)	Test 3	(Purcell)
Test 84	Chorale prelude (Bach)	Test 26	(Bach, arranged Busoni)
Test 85	Baroque sacred cantata (Bach)		
	compared with secular cantata	Test 4	(Arne)
Test 90	Classical minuet (Haydn)	Test 11	(Boccherini)
Test 92	Classical rondo (Beethoven)	Test 12	(Haydn) and Test 22 (Crusell)
	compared with Baroque *rondeau*	Test 2	(Purcell)
Test 93	Classical symphony (Haydn)	Test 12	(Haydn)
Test 94	Thematic transformation (Berlioz)	Test 18	(Rimsky-Korsakov)
	Berlioz's style compared with Mendelssohn	Test 24	(Mendelssohn)
Test 95	Romantic Lieder (Schubert)	Test 20	(Schubert, with Italian text)
	compared with Schumann	Test 14	(Schumann)
	compared with popular song	Test 17	(French)
Test 98	Romantic violin sonata (Brahms)		
	compared with Baroque violin sonata	Test 21	(Corelli)
	compared with Romantic chamber music	Test 23	(Dvořák) and Test 24 (Mendelssohn)
Test 99	Romantic characteristic dances (Chopin)	Test 15	(Liszt)
Test 101	Russian music (Tchaikovsky)	Test 18	(Rimsky-Korsakov)
Test 105	French piano music (Debussy)	Test 13	(Satie, orchestrated Debussy)
Test 106	20th-century organ music (Messiaen)		
	compared with Romantic organ music	Test 28	(Lefébure-Wély)
Test 109	English 20th-century vocal music (Britten)	Test 25	(Farrar)
Test 110	Shostakovich	Test 16	(Shostakovich)
	concerto compared with Rimsky-Korsakov	Test 18	(Rimsky-Korsakov)
Test 111	Modern *a cappella* vocal music (Tavener)		
	compared with earlier *a cappella* styles	Test 10	(Bruckner) and Test 19 (Tallis)

The model answers given below are intended primarily to assist teachers and students working through the bank of tests in this volume. They do not represent the only answers that would be acceptable in a public examination. Responses that are accurate and unambiguous, or which make reference to different (but valid) points in answer to the question posed, always receive credit in the mark-schemes for such examinations.

Suggested marks are shown to the right of each question, and to the right of each answer below. Again, these are provided to help teachers weight marks appropriately to the degree of perception needed to answer each individual question. They do not necessarily represent the mark weightings that might be applied in public examinations. Parts of answers within brackets are for reference, and should not be considered essential when awarding marks. Alternative answers are separated by diagonal slashes—*exact* synonyms should also be accepted. Marks in brackets show if, and how, credit may be awarded for part answers. Underlined words (or their synonyms) are obligatory if that part of the answer is to receive credit. Please note that in operational examinations, various alternative answers which are not encompassed by the original mark-scheme are always considered, and may be added to the mark-scheme if they offer a valid and accurate response to the question set.

In addition to the identification of the source of each extract, brief commentaries have been provided, offering further information for any discussion arising from listening to the extracts and including comparisons with various related works. The latter have been limited to examples in the companion volumes, **Aural Matters** and **Sound Matters** (see Introduction), together with examples in the popular London Anthology of Music (**LAM**—published by the University of London Examinations and Assessment Council) and a few other works which, in the experience of the authors, are often available in schools. It is intended that these comparisons should be used to enlarge the *aural* experience of students, by listening and discussion, and as such they should lead the student towards a greater awareness of what is typical, what is unusual and what is unique in the stylistic analysis of the music studied.

Test 1   Marks

(a) the opening trumpet motif / imitation of the first trumpet   1
(b) trombone   1
(c) trill   1
(d) they are in parallel <u>thirds</u>   1
(e) bar 5, penultimate semiquaver (F sharp)   1
(f) bar 7   1
(g) dominant / F sharp (1), leaps down an octave (1), then tonic / B (1)   Maximum 2
(h) an echo (1) of the previous four beats (accept 'previous bar') (1)   2
(i) it uses entirely chord I / the tonic / a chord of B (2) or it uses only one chord (=1)   2
(j) strings / violins   1
(k) concerto (1) grosso (1)   2

Source Nicola Matteis: Concerto in C, first movement (?1685)

Commentary Nicola Matteis (c.1650–?1707) was one of many foreign musicians who settled in London in the years after the Restoration. This recording is a conjectural reconstruction of a concerto that may have been written before 1685. What is certain is that Matteis, like many Baroque composers, published the music for various instrumental forces to maximize sales, including a solo violin version *ad immitatione della Trombetta* (1685) and a trio version for three trumpets, enigmatically entitled *Concerto ... con violini e Flauti* (1687). The third trumpet part is unplayable on the natural trumpet and is given, in this performance, to a trombone. Although unusual in this type of music, the trombone is not an implausible choice—it was popular in Matteis's native Italy and had been specifically referenced by its English name of 'sackbut' in Locke's *Music ffor His Majesty's Sagbutts and Cornetts* of 1661. The string and continuo parts in the recording are an editorial recreation. The original music was in the key of C—the transposition to B in this performance reflects the fact that Baroque pitch was lower than modern standards.

The movement is the first of seven—mostly short binary forms, with or without a tiny fanfare-like coda. This, plus the date and lack of real contrast between the brass and string groups, places the work in the style of the early concerto grosso—compare the movement with the binary-form Allegro from Corelli's contemporary Concerto Grosso Op. 6 No. 8 in **LAM 17** or with the movement in **Test 21** below. Matteis's simple style highlights some of the reasons why Corelli's relative sophistication made such an impact on late-Baroque composers. The very simple harmony is, of course, a function of the available notes on the natural trumpet, but Matteis shows little invention in getting round this limitation—compare Handel's trumpet writing in **Sound Matters 19** or Bach's in works such as the Second 'Brandenburg' Concerto and Magnificat. Examples of the later type of Baroque concerto grosso favoured by Vivaldi and Bach, with three much more extended movements, are given in **Aural Matters Test 82** and **Sound Matters 12**.

Test 2   Marks

(a) (i)   (ascending) minor (1) triad (1)   2
    (ii)   descending (1) one-bar (1) sequence (1) of a triadic (1) motif   Maximum 3
    (iii) hemiola / four quavers plus two crotchets / four semiquavers plus two quavers   1
(b) (i)   (the same melody) transposed / in the relative major   1
    (ii)   it also contains (one-bar) sequences   1
(c) (i)   conjunct (instead of triadic) / including dotted rhythms / ending with an imperfect cadence   1
    (ii)   minor (instead of major) (1) and modulates (1) (back to tonic)   2
(d) homophonic (1) four-part (1) texture of strings (1) and harpsichord (1)
    played on 'authentic' instruments (1)   Maximum 4

Source Henry Purcell: *Rondeau* from the incidental music for *Abdelazar, or The Moor's Revenge* (1695)

Commentary The Baroque *rondeau* was cultivated in France. The refrain (called the *grand couplet* or *rondeau*) always remained in the tonic. Repetitions of the *grand couplet* were separated from each other by contrasting episodes (called *couplets*) in related keys. Further examples of the *rondeau* will be found in **Sound Matters 17** (Couperin) and **LAM 32** (Rameau). The expression 'en rondeau' was often appended to dances that use the form—this movement by Purcell is effectively a 'minuet en rondeau'. Having completed this test, further work could be done by studying the use made of Purcell's refrain in *The Young Person's Guide to the Orchestra* by Benjamin Britten, where it forms the basis for a set of variations—it is also fashioned into a fugal subject towards the end of the work, the fugue reaching its climax with an augmentation of Purcell's theme in the major key, played by the trombones.

Test 3   Marks

(a) cello (1) organ (1) (arch)lute (1)   3
(b) with a melisma   1
(c) a (semiquaver rising) scale is added (to the word 'a' in the second statement of 'a prince')   1

(d) (rising) triads (1) are repeated in descending (1) sequences (1) 3
(e) the sequences are now ascending / the key is now major 1
(f) it has the same bass part 1
(g) it is an almost exact <u>repeat of the entire vocal section</u> 1
(h) ground bass 1
(i) (Henry) Purcell or any English contemporary (1)　　　1695—accept any date between 1660 and 1710 (1) 2

Source Henry Purcell: 'A Prince of Glorious Race' from *Ode for the Duke of Gloucester's Birthday* (1695)

Commentary Purcell was in his own time, and still is, justly famous for his imaginative handling of the ground bass. The ground may be repeated throughout an entire movement (e.g., **Sound Matters 11** and **LAM 21**) or, as here, it may be modified to allow modulation away from the original key. In longer songs the ground may be abandoned altogether for dramatic effect (e.g., 'The Plaint' from *The Fairy Queen*, part of which appears in **Aural Matters Test 83**). The first part of 'A Prince of Glorious Race' is, of course, accompanied by the continuo instruments alone. As in almost all such Baroque music, the composer notated this in only two parts—vocal line and bass—and the organ and archlute are therefore improvising harmonies derived from the bass. A further example of Baroque-style improvisation can be heard in the ornamentation of the vocal part when sections are repeated, as happens on the words 'A prince', 'happy' and 'birth'. The work from which this song is taken is described as an 'ode'—a type of English secular cantata (see also **Test 4** below). Purcell's best-known odes are perhaps 'Hail! Bright Cecilia' (see **Sound Matters 11**) and 'Come, Ye Sons of Art' (with its famous duet for two counter-tenors, 'Sound The Trumpet').

Test 4	Marks

(a) they are divided into semiquavers / slow measured tremolo 1
(b) descending (major) scale 1
(c) suspensions 1
(d) it uses the same ascending tonic triad / the first six (or seven) pitches are identical 1
(e) ascending arpeggios (1) crescendo (1) melodic line rises to high register (1) Maximum 2
(f) (i)　<u>falling appoggiatura / appoggiatura and trill</u> (1)
　　(ii)　rising appoggiatura (1)　　　(iii) slide / passing notes / triplet / falling scale (1) 3
(g) (i)　a rising (1) real/modulating (1) sequence　　(ii) an ascending (1) chromatic scale (1) Maximum 3
(h) a 4–3 suspension 1
(i) Arne / Boyce / Handel (1)　　　1755—accept any date between 1715 and 1765 (1) 2

Source Thomas Arne: 'The Glitt'ring Sun' from *The Morning* (No. 5 of Six English Cantatas, 1755).

Commentary Thomas Arne (1710–1778), now best known as the composer of *Rule, Brittania* and of songs for Shakespeare's plays, was the leading English theatrical composer of the mid-18th century. This cantata was written for the Vauxhall Pleasure Gardens in London, scene of the first public rehearsal of Handel's 'Fireworks Music' six years earlier. The extracts for **Tests 3, 4 and 5** illustrate some of the changing fashions in English secular music over the period 1695–1769—essentially from mid-Baroque style through to the *style galant*. This particular piece offers some helpfully clear examples of appropriate vocal ornamentation of a Baroque composer's basic text. Compare Arne's writing with the vocal music of Handel (**Aural Matters Test 86**, **Sound Matters 13**, **LAM 26**), and contrast the style of both composers with arias from sacred cantatas by Bach (**Sound Matters 15**, **LAM 25**), particularly noting Bach's preference for long, contrapuntal lines in both the vocal part and the accompaniment.

Test 5	Marks

(a) two oboes (1) two horns (1) bassoon (1) 3
(b) (i)　strings (1)　　　the dominant / C sharp (major) (1) 2
　　(ii)　(mezzo-)soprano (1)　　　wind / oboes and horn (1) 2
　　　　secondary (1) dominant (1) – tonic (1)　　or modulating (1) sequences (1) Maximum 2
　　(iii)　soprano (1)　　　relative minor / D sharp minor (1) 2
　　　　conjunct motion / scale patterns /
　　　　crotchet–quaver rhythm 1
　　(iv)　tenor (1)　　　a tonic pedal / the primary triads (1) 2
　　　　imperfect 1
(c) (i)　the introduction / first two lines of verse 1 (1)　(ii) four-voice (1) homophony (1) Maximum 2
　　(iii)　alternate upper and lower pairs of voices (1)　(iv) a cadential 6–4 / F sharp/C sharp (1) 2
(d) 1769—accept any date between 1740 and 1790 1

Source Charles Dibdin: *The Ephesian Matron*—vaudeville finale (1769).

Commentary Charles Dibdin (1745–1814) was possibly as colourful, prolific and irascible a figure in London opera houses of the late-18th century as Handel had been fifty years before. Both composer and impresario, Dibdin also twice ran up enormous debts on failed enterprises. His many talents, though, were perhaps spread too widely—he was also a singer, dramatist, poet, novelist, artist and publisher, excelling in no one field. Dibdin's later music fails to fulfil the promise of his early works, although the melody of his song *Tom Bowling* (dating from the Napoleonic wars) still gets annual exposure in Henry Wood's *Fantasia on British Sea Songs* at the Last Night of the Proms.

Dibdin wrote for Covent Garden and for Garrick, the famous actor-manager at Drury Lane, but *The Ephesian Matron* was composed for Ranelagh Gardens, rival venue to Vauxhall (see commentary to **Test 4**). The limited facilities there doubtless dictated a total cast of just the four characters heard in this extract. Spoken dialogue was banned at Ranelagh, and the opera is thus sung throughout, with recitatives interpolated between some ten arias, a duet and this ensemble. The work is therefore not a ballad opera (nor does it contain contemporary popular tunes), but a later stage towards the creation of an English comic-opera style—a development that was to lie largely dormant until the operettas of Sullivan in the late-19th century. There is no surving full score of the work, and the original vocal score of this movement is in G: the transposition down a semitone in this performance reflects the lower pitch standard of music at the time. The melody-dominated style, with its parallel thirds, periodic phrasing and light accompaniment of functional harmonies, together with the prominent use of oboes and horns in the orchestration, are clear pointers to the *style galant* (see **Aural Matters, page 111**). Yet students might almost be forgiven for thinking that this extract is by 'G & S': the same *galant* features were still part of the mercurial Sullivan's vocabulary over a century later.

The extract is a 'vaudeville finale'—one in which all of the characters reappear to take a verse each, usually expressing a moral, between the tutti refrains. It became one of the great clichés of opera and had a lasting, if not altogether welcome, influence on works as diverse as Gluck's *Orfeo*, Mozart's *Don Giovanni* and even Verdi's *Falstaff*. Contrasting this extract with Arne's more serious work in **Test 4** will help point the transition from late-Baroque to *galant* style, and comparison with Martini's gavotte in **Aural Matters Test 81** will underline some of the salient features of the new music. Comparison with Mozart is harsh on Dibdin, but **Sound Matters 23** will illustrate just some of the ways in which one of the greatest of operatic composers handled light operatic material only 22 years later.

Test 6			Marks
(a)	(i)	'(For he that) is mighty hath magnified me' / '(And hath) exalted the humble and meek'	1
	(ii)	'And holy is his name'	1
(b)	(i)	the bass sustains a tonic (1) pedal (1)	2
	(ii)	appoggiatura	1
(c)		four–six part / soloist plus choir (1) *a capella* (1) homophony (1)	3
(d)	(i)	the solo forms an inverted (1) and decorated (1) pedal (1) against the harmony	Maximum 2
	(ii)	the trebles repeat the solo part in a (descending) sequence	1
(e)		arpeggios (1) in staccato (1) quavers (1)	3

Test 6a					Marks
(f)	(i)	'forefathers' (1)	(ii)	'for ever' (1)	2
(g)		all voices in octaves (2) / unison (1)			2
(h)	(i)	imperfect (1)	(ii) perfect (1)	(iii) plagal (1)	3
(i)	(i)	it is in triple metre / the metre appears to change between three and four beats per bar			1
	(ii)	the arpeggiated obbligato part is omitted / it is much louder			1
(j)		Brahms			1

Source Charles Villiers Stanford: Magnificat, from Magnificat and Nunc Dimittis in G major (1903).

Commentary Stanford (1852–1924) studied in Germany, where he absorbed many features of Brahms's style: the extract from Brahms's Violin Sonata in G (**Aural Matters Test 98**) demonstrates some of the similarities between the music of the two composers. As Professor of Music at Cambridge and Professor of Composition at the Royal College of Music he was influential in the early 20th-century rebirth of English music, and his compositions for the Anglican Church are still in the repertoire of cathedrals and churches throughout the world. The Magnificat is the song of the Blessed Virgin Mary (Luke I: 46–55) which is sung in Latin in the Roman Catholic evening service of Vespers, and in English in the Anglican service of Evensong. It has been suggested that the combination of treble soloist and quaver organ obbligato in this setting is intended to symbolize Mary happily singing Magnificat as she sits at a spinning wheel—a similar technique, but used in a very different context, to Gretchen's anguished spinning in the accompaniment of Schubert's Lied *Gretchen am Spinnrade* (see **Aural Matters, page 131**).

Test 7		Marks
(a)	basses	1
(b)	seven—accept any number between five and eight	1
(c)	(i) 3 (ii) 4 (iii) 2 (iv) 4 (1 mark for each)	4
(d)	by contrapuntal <u>overlapping</u> of the end of each phrase with the start of the next	1
(e)	suspension	1
(f)	major with occasional flattened sevenths	1
(g)	16th century	1

Source John Sheppard: The first setting of the antiphon for Trinity Sunday, *Libera nos, salva nos*.

Commentary An antiphon is a short liturgical chant often sung in association with a psalm. In churches with a choral foundation, and for important feasts, the plainsong could be replaced by a polyphonic setting often, as here, with the original plainsong used as a cantus firmus. John Sheppard (c.1515–1558) was Master of the Choristers at Magdalen College, Oxford and later a Gentleman of the Chapel Royal. More of his music survives than that of any of his English contemporaries. His style is similar to that of Tallis, but it tends to be more continuously imitative, and the seamless polyphony is more often constructed around a plainsong cantus firmus—compare this antiphon with the motet by Tallis on **Track 19** of the accompanying CD. The date of this work is not known, but it was most probably written for the Chapel Royal in the period 1553–1558, when the Latin liturgy was briefly resumed during the reign of Queen Mary.

Test 8		Marks
(a)	C (1) and G (1)—accept 'tonic and dominant', despite the modality of the piece	2
(b)	<u>D</u> crotchet (instead of the E in the first phrase)	1
(c)	triplet omitted / minim G	1
(d)	<u>B flat</u>	1
(e)	an anacrusis / pair of quavers	1
(f)	AAB [The medieval 'bar' form]	1
(g)	a (major) sixth / B flat to G	1

(h) (contr)alto   **1**
(i) Mixolydian   **2**
(j) (i) monophonic   **1**
    (ii) imitation (or passing notes) at phrase ends / occasional chords / heterophony / percussion   Maximum **1**
(k) use of bowed string instrument / voice joins in for third phrase / ornamentation   Maximum **2**

Source Martin Codax: *Mandad' ei comigo* (Cantiga II from *Cantigas de Amigo*)

Commentary See page 13. The repetitive nature of the song may suggest that three complete playings is unnecessary for this item. As with much medieval music, precise dating is impossible. Most authorities, however, believe the work to come from before the early 14th-century date given in the CD booklet. For elaborated performance versions of other monophonic music compare **Aural Matters Test 38** and **Sound Matters 5a**.

Test 9   Marks

(a) passing notes / a scale figure   **1**
(b) the middle voice overlaps the rest (1), the bass moves with rhythmic interest across the gap (1)   **2**
(c) imitation (1) at the octave (1) at a distance of a minim (1)   Maximum **2**
(d) the fourth degree of the mode is sharpened (F sharp) / the music modulates to the dominant (G)   **1**
(e) it is used in sequence (1) a note lower (1) and in imitation (1) only one crotchet later (1)
    in the top voice (1), where it also reappears immediately in sequence (1)   Maximum **3**
(f) major triad (1) at (f), bare octaves (1) at the end   **2**
(g) augmented fourth / diminished fifth / tritone / *diabolus in musica*   **1**
(h) (i) 9–8 (1)   (ii) 4–3 (1)   **2**

Source *Ma dame, trop vous mesprenés*—late-15th century, from the court of (or by) Charles the Bold, Duke of Burgundy

Commentary See page 13. The word *chanson* has as many meanings as the word 'song', but is usually used to refer to secular French polyphonic settings of the 15th and 16th centuries. There are notable stylistic differences across this 200-year period. The *chansons* of the Burgundian (or Franco-Netherlands) period tend to use chivalrous poetry set to a three-voice, treble-dominated texture. Dufay is the most famous practitioner of this type, and the influence of his style, particularly the use of tiny rhythmic cells that seem almost to float free of the underlying metre, is still evident in the *chanson* on this track. Parisian *chansons* of the 16th century are usually four- or five-voice settings of much more popular, metrical verse (sometimes bawdy, sometimes highly descriptive). Clear-cut rhythms, triad-based harmony, distinct sections of counterpoint and homophony, and repeating refrains all reveal the influence of the canzonet and ballett in these later works, although the genre retained the melody-dominated texture and never sought the equal-voice polyphony of the serious madrigal.

Test 10   Marks

(a) (i) the melody begins a tone higher (1) / its third note repeats the second note (1)
    it descends a third (1) instead of a fourth / it is harmonized in the dominant (1)   Maximum **3**
    (ii) z   **1**
(b) (i) the printed melody is repeated in sequence (1) up a tone (1)   **2**
    (ii) the soprano (freely) imitates the bass   **1**
(c) (i) the printed music is repeated twice (1) in a descending (1) sequence (1)
    outlining a chromatic (1) scale   Maximum **2**
    (ii) the soprano imitates (1) the tenor by inversion (1)   **2**
(d) ternary   **1**
(e) motet (2) / anthem (1)   **2**
(f) Bruckner   **1**

Source Anton Bruckner: *Locus iste a Deo factus est* (1869)

Commentary Anton Bruckner (1824–1896) was amongst the most important composers of church music in the 19th century. A glance at **LAM 71** (from his Mass in E minor of the same year) reveals the two opposing styles of composition that permeate so much of Bruckner's music. On the one hand, the Sanctus is almost Renaissance-like in its unaccompanied eight-part imitative polyphony (built on a theme from a mass by Palestrina). On the other hand, the Benedictus is extremely chromatic in both melody and harmony; it is much more homophonic and is accompanied by wind instruments. *Locus iste*, although one of Bruckner's simpler motets, inclines towards this latter style, with rich chromaticism surrounded by the diatonic, functional harmony of its outer sections. The comparatively limited use of imitative polyphony enhances the motet's declamatory style, rather than creating the seamless texture of much Renaissance music (compare the motet by Sheppard in **Test 7** above). It is, of course, important that students can recognize the 19th-century harmonic style of this motet, and do not assume that all *a capella* church music with Latin words must originate from the Renaissance. This test should provide a good opportunity to check that they are registering *all* aspects of the music, and not just relying on its more superficial facets for identification.

Test 11   Marks

(a) oboe (1) playing in octaves (1) with the violins   **2**
(b) Ic / A/E / E$^6_4$ / (1) + V / E (1) or feminine (1) imperfect cadence / cadential 6-4 (1)   **2**
(c) horns (1) playing the dominant / an inner pedal (1)   **2**
(d) V / E + I / A (1) or perfect cadence (1)   **1**
(e) a repeat of the previous four bars   **1**
(f) (all instruments) in octaves (2) / in unison (1)   **2**
(g) augmented sixth   **1**
(h) repeat of lines 1–3 / bars 1–16   **1**

(i) symphony / serenade / divertimento   **1**
(j) minuet   **1**
(k) 1775—accept any date between 1750 and 1800   **1**

Source Luigi Boccherini: Minuet from Sinfonia 14 in A, Op. 21 No. 6, Gérard catalogue 498 (1775).

Commentary Luigi Boccherini (1743–1805) was one of the most pre-eminent Italian composers of the Classical period. However, this symphony could almost as well have come from the pen of Haydn writing in the mid–1770s (a contemporary rather cruelly refered to Boccherini as 'Haydn's wife'). The *galant* style, with its periodic phrasing, feminine cadences, melody-dominated homophony and clear tonal schemes—together with the chamber instrumentation (two horns, two oboes and strings) and scoring—are all typical of this decade of the 18th century. However, 'Haydn's wife' was not capable of Haydn's own intensity (exemplified by the latter's *Sturm und Drang* symphonies—compare the dramatic minuet of Haydn's 'La Passione' Symphony in **Sound Matters 20** or the forceful 'Lamentatione' Symphony given in full in **LAM 40**)—nor of Haydn's more 'masculine' driving rhythms and intricate motivic unity exemplified by the first movement of the 'Drumroll' (**Aural Matters Tracks 33–35**) and the finale of the 'Surprise', which is the subject of **Test 12** below.

Test 12   **Marks**

(a) a flute (1) doubles the melody at the octave above (1)   2
(b) the previous two bars are repeated in descending (1) sequence (1)   2
(c) (i) it becomes a scale (1) figure   (ii) bassoon (1)   2
(d) (i) y^1 (ii) x (iii) z (iv) w (1 mark for each in correct order)   4
(e) imperfect   1

Test 12a   **Marks**

(f) (i) y^1 (1)   (ii) it has been inverted (1)   2
(g) x 1
(h) tonic (1) pedal (1) played by pizzicato (1) double basses (1) with chords I (1) and $V^{(7)}$ (1) above   Maximum 5
(i) I (1), IV (1) and V (1)—a mark may be awarded for Ic if offered as distinct from I   Maximum 3

Test 12b   **Marks**

(j) (i) violins (1) and bassoon (1)   2
     (ii) the music of the transition begins (1) before the phrase has ended / with an overlapping phrase (1)   2
(k) strings: scales (1) semiquavers (1) counterpoint (1)   wind: sustained (1) chords (1)   Maximum 2
(l) it is the same   1
(m) it is now in the tonic (1) minor (1)   2

Test 12c   **Marks**

(n) (i) w (1) and z (1)   (ii) they sustain a tonic (1) pedal (1)   4
(o) (i) unrelated key (1), flat submediant / E flat (2), a tertiary modulation (2)   Maximum 2
     (ii) entirely diatonic (1), repetitions of the tonic chord (1), G major scales (1) and
           repeated perfect cadences (1)   Maximum 2
(p) elements of rondo form (2) / it is in sonata-rondo form (2) / abridged development (1)   Maximum 2

Source Joseph Haydn: Symphony No. 94 in G major ('Surprise')—finale (1791)

Commentary Haydn so saturated some of his movements with motifs or variants of motifs from a single initial theme that some commentators have described them as 'monothematic'. Be that as it may, this technique should not be confused with Baroque monothematicism. In the latter the consistent deployment of a limited number of figures results in static forms which explore only one affection. Haydn, in contrast, relies as much as any Classical composer on the dramatic opposition of tonal centres and contrasting affections—compare the driving rhythms of the G major first subject with the lyrical D major of the second. Sometimes he uses huge tonal shifts, not primarily for structural purposes but as a means of engendering a feeling of conflict which, when released, creates a climax of excitement. In the coda, the eruption from G major into E flat and back will ensure as much rapturous applause as the frenetic semiquaver runs and the silly quiet woodwind cadence before the *fortissimo* ending.

Students can be mystified by the references in textbooks to Haydn's humour, especially in finales like this. Music is not, of course, an art that lends itself to gut-busting jokes. Even the famous feature in the slow movement of this symphony is one of surprise (hence the work's nickname) rather than hilarity. Haydn's wit is the humour of whimsy—the unexpected turning, the unusual viewpoint, the improbable development. These features are also fundamental in avoiding the potential clichés of the Classical style, and they abound in this, as in all of the 'London' symphonies.

Like most of Haydn's finales (in fact, like most movements by even modestly talented Classical composers) this Allegro cannot be pigeon-holed according to 19th-century concepts of late 18th-century formal procedures. In broad outline it conforms to sonata form, but the rondo-like theme pops up all over the place, like a rabbit peaking out of different exits from its burrow. This is not textbook sonata-rondo form (ABACABA in which A and B are the first and second subjects and C is the development) since the first-subject-cum-rondo theme invades the 'development' and the 'transition' dwarfs the tiny second subject. For comparisons, see the commentary on **Test 11**.

Test 13   **Marks**

(a) (i) <u>suspended</u> cymbal (1)   (ii) struck with a soft beater / timpani stick (1)   (iii) third (1)   3
(b) (i) duplicated an <u>octave higher</u> (1)   (ii) harp <u>arpeggios</u> (1)   2
(c) (i) horn (1)   (ii) *bouché* / (hand-)stopped (2) ('muted'=1)   (iii) it plays repeated / untied F sharps (1)   4
(d) (i) oboe (1)   (ii) violins <u>and violas</u> / mid-range strings (1)   2

(e)   it forms a pedal / repeated pitches of D   1
(f)   (i)   violins / strings (in octaves) (1)   (ii)   horn (1)   2
(g)   C (1) natural (1)   2

Source   Erik Satie: *Gymnopédie* No. 1 (1888), originally for piano. This version orchestrated by Debussy (1896).

Commentary   Satie wrote three *Gymnopédies* for piano, each taking a slightly different approach to basically similar material. The title refers to the hypnotic, ritual dances in honour of Apollo, performed by naked youths at Sparta in ancient Greece. Debussy scored the first and third of Satie's pieces, reversing their order of performance. Dynamics and phrasing have been reproduced from the first edition of the work (echoed in Debussy's version) although both are absent in Satie's original manuscript.

No question on dating has been set, since Satie's forward-looking style is not readily associated with the late-Romantic period from which this music emanates. Satie's original version can be played on the piano from the score reproduced in this book, for the purpose of comparison. Other well-known examples of orchestrations of piano music include Mussorgsky's *Pictures at an Exhibition* (orchestrated by Ravel, Funteck and others), Grieg's orchestration of his Holberg and Lyric Suites, or Brahms's orchestration of his Three Hungarian Dances, originally for piano duet.

Test 14   Marks

(a)   (i)   in thirds / sixths with the melody (1)   (ii)   I (1) and V$^{(7)}$ (1)   3
      (iii) 5 / 6 / 7 / 13 /14 / 15 (1)   (iv)   the same music as the introduction (1)   2
      (v)   interrupted   1
(b)   (i)   the key changes to the flat submediant / C (major) (3) / tertiary modulation (2) / unrelated key (1)   3
      (ii)   a tonic (1) pedal (1)   2
(c)   (i)   it returns to the same key / tonic / E (major)   1
      (ii)   the key changes to tonic minor (1) and the accompaniment becomes staccato / detached chords (1)   2
(d)   (i)   higher tessitura (1)   (ii)   chromaticism (1)   2

Source   Robert Schumann: *Waldesgespräch* from the song-cycle, *Liederkreis*, Op. 77 No. 3 (1840)

Commentary   Schumann's idiomatic piano writing (which often leads the voice) is apparent only in the the repetition of the four-bar introduction to Eichendorff's poem and the rhetorical piano postlude based on the same material. Even here, the understated, filigree arpeggiation typical of so many of his songs is replaced by a dramatic directness that could easily be mistaken for Schubert—and thus a 'spot the composer' question seems inappropriate. Compare this song with **Sound Matters 26** (*Am Meer*), in which Schubert's tonal scheme in a four-stanza poem is similar to this setting, and **LAM 56** (*Der Doppelgänger*), where Schubert reserves his D sharp minor tonal fireworks for one of the most climactic points in Western music. Schumann's tiny 'Du Ring an meinem Finger' (**LAM 61**, dating from the same *annus mirabilis* as *Waldesgespräch)* pales into insignificance among such masterpieces.

Test 15   Marks

(a)   (i)   an acciaccatura / crushed note (1)   (ii)   he doubles the melody (1) at the upper octave (1)   3
      (iii) he anticipates the second beat of bar 3 (1) and delays the third beat of bar 4 (1) / rubato (=1 only)   2
      (iv)   I / A (1) and V^7 / E^7 (1)   2
(b)   (i)   they all begin with the same four bars   1
      (ii)   harmony: more chromatic (1)   tonality: the music modulates to a new key (1)   2
(c)   (i)   the same progression is used in sequence (1), a minor third lower / in A minor (1)   2
      (ii)   Ic / cadential second inversion   1
(d)   (i)   he uses rubato (1) throughout the piece   (ii)   a waltz (1)   2
      (iii) Liszt—accept any piano composer flourishing in the period 1820–1897 (1)
             1842—accept any date between 1820 and 1897 (1)   2

Source   Franz Liszt: *Albumblatt in Walzerform* (Album leaf in the form of a waltz)

Commentary   Liszt, like all Romantic piano composers, satisfied the huge demand for short, relatively simple salon music by writing characteristic pieces. These could be poetic meditations upon a particular mood, or literary or artistic subject—or they could, like this waltz, be dances. The subject is discussed more fully on pages 137–141 of **Aural Matters** and **Test 99** of that book offers a comparison with a mazurka by Chopin. Reference should also be made to **Sound Matters 28** and **29**. The title 'Album leaf' referred originally to the practice of writing such pieces into the music album of a friend or patron. Perhaps the most famous example is Beethoven's *Albumblatt für Elise*.

Test 16   Marks

(a)   a tonic (1) pedal (1)   2
(b)   beats 3 and 4 reversed (1) submediant / (allow 'relative minor') pedal (1)   2
(c)   inversion   1
(d)   (descending) triad of C (1) major (1) / sequence (1) down a semitone (1)   2
(e)   chromatic   1
(f)   Neapolitan sixth   1
(g)   semitone lower (1) after the printed first four notes [it is also clearly displaced by one beat]   1
(h)   triple / $\frac{9}{8}$ 1
(i)   inverted (1) dominant (1) pedal (1)   3

Test 16a   Marks

(j)   (i)   same (1)   (ii)   simple / $\frac{2}{4}$ / $\frac{4}{4}$ etc. (1)   (iii)   entirely contrapuntal / three-part / fugal (1)   3
(k)   entirely (1) triadic / chordal / only one chord (1)   2
(l)   very slow   1

(m) a tertiary modulation	1
(n) circle/cycle of fifths	1
(o) dominant (1) pedal (1)	2
(p) stretto (1) / inversion (1) / augmentation (1) / fragmentation (1)	Maximum 2
(q) fugue	1

Source Dimitri Shostakovich: Prelude and Fugue in A, Op. 87 No. 7 (1950/51)

Commentary This is one of a set of 24 Preludes and Fugues for piano, and is performed on the accompanying CD by Tatiana Nikolayeva—the pianist whose playing of Bach inspired the composition and who gave its first performance. In **Aural Matters (page 152)** we mentioned the communist attack on Shostakovich's music following the première of *Lady Macbeth* in 1936. A more wide-ranging purge followed in 1948, embracing Prokofiev and other leading Soviet composers accused of representing 'the cult of atonality, discord and dissonance'. Shostakovich was obliged to recant: 'I know that the party is right … I am deeply grateful for the criticism'. For the next few years he withheld new compositions that were likely to cause controversy, at the same time developing a more popularist idiom for public works, particularly in his film scores and vocal music. The Prelude and Fugue in A dates from this period of sunny diatonicism and makes a vivid comparison with the gloom of the composer's First Cello Concerto (**Aural Matters Test 110**), written at the end of the decade. Shostakovich does not draw on Bach merely for the form—compare the Prelude with Bach's D major Prelude from Book II of the '48'—although Shostakovich's neo-classical style always presents some unexpected turn in harmony, melody or tonality. The audacious attempt to build the fugue subject entirely on a tonic chord of A might seem almost to poke fun at politically-engineered attempts to banish dissonance. The piece should, at least, generate discussion on whether this music 'works' as a fugue—compare it with the much more linear approach, depending on constant passing notes, dissonance and resolution, of the Baroque fugues in **LAM 24**, **Sound Matters 12** or **Aural Matters Test 79**.

Test 17	**Marks**
(a) 5/7 (1) and 8 (1)	2
(b) dominant (1) seventh (1)	2
(c) an octave	1
(d) line 2: imperfect (1), line 4: perfect (1)	2
(e) (i) 4 (1) (ii) 6 (1)	2
(f) by adding extra notes / grace notes / slides (1) in the bass / left hand (1)	2
(g) 1–4	1
(h) triplets	1
(i) (i) repeated chords, rather than alternating bass notes and chords (1) (ii) higher register (1)	2
(j) the dominant	1

Source Percy French: *Phil The Fluter's Ball* (1889), (music-hall) song for voice and piano.

Commentary See the panel following Test 17. While this song is of a type that may not be set in examinations which restrict the study of popular music to the late-20th century, the techniques so clearly expounded in the music and referenced in the questions will be encountered in many other styles—this, plus the helpfully repetitive strophic form, may suggest the song as being of particular use in the early stages of an aural course. A comparison with 19th-century art songs (e.g., **Test 14** above or **LAM 79**), will reveal the more subtle rôle of the piano in Lieder. The style here is in many respects much closer to that of contemporary industrial folk-song (e.g., *Poverty Knock*, **Aural Matters Test 46**).

Test 18	**Marks**
(a) y	1
(b) dominant (1) sevenths (1)	2
(c) whole tone	2
(d) real/modulating (1) sequence (1) a tone lower (1)	Maximum 2
(e) z	1
(f) x (1) (ii) diminution (1)	2
(g) flute (1) and clarinet (1) alternate (1)	3
(h) imperfect / Phrygian (1) in C sharp minor / relative minor (1)	2
(i) imitation	1

Test 18a	**Marks**
(j) (i) free inversion (1) (ii) sequence of bars 1–4 (1) (iii) first bar repeated in sequence (1)	3
(k) the theme printed under question (j)	1
(l) D flat major	1
(m) Saint-Saëns / Rimsky-Korsakov / Tchaikovsky / Rachmaninov (1) 1882/3—accept any date between 1860 and 1910 (1)	2

Source Nikolai Rimsky-Korsakov: Piano Concerto in C sharp minor, Op. 30 (final Allegro, cadenza and coda).

Commentary Pupil of Balakirev; friend of Mussorgsky, Cui, Borodin and Tchaikovsky; teacher of Glazunov, Stravinsky and Prokofiev—Rimsky-Korsakov occupies a central position between the 19th- and 20th-century Russian nationalists. He was an enthusiast for the music of Berlioz and Liszt, and dedicated this concerto to the memory of the latter when it was published in 1886. Liszt's influence is seen in the 'all in one' single-movement structure of the concerto and in its use of thematic transformation—see question (j) above. Indeed, almost all of the thematic material in the entire work is derived from the Russian folk tune printed on page 32. The short, wistful motifs—almost modal in quality—repeated and treated in sequence over richly chromatic harmonies, with a preference for rhythmic (rather than pitch-based) transformations, are all typical of the Russian school and should prove to be key factors in identification (see **Aural Matters page 140**). A comparison with the piano concertos of Mozart (**Sound Matters 22,**

LAM 45) will reveal some of the enormous stylistic changes in the genre over the intervening century. Richard Strauss's First Horn Concerto (**LAM 75**), composed over the same two years, offers a much closer comparison.

Test 19	Marks
(a) a suspension	1
(b) it is exactly the same as the previous phrase / the first four bars of the soprano part	1
(c) the first interval is expanded to a fourth (1)—allow 'first part of the phrase is higher', but not 'sequence' both syllables of *pandis* are sung to longer notes (1)	2
(d) simultaneous (1) false relation / use of raised and lowered seventh degree of the scale (1)	2
(e) Dorian mode	1
(f) (i) the sixth (in *Da robur fer*) (1) and the third (which forms a *tierce de Picardie* in the final chord) (1)	2
(ii) the sixth has been flattened (1) and the third has been sharpened (1)	2
(g) treble / <u>boy</u> soprano (1), counter-tenor / <u>male</u> alto (1), tenor (1), baritone (1), bass (1)	5
(h) imitative (1) polyphonic (1)	2

Source Thomas Tallis: *O Salutaris hostia* (c.1570)

Commentary There are at least eight 16th- and early 17th-century sources for this motet, including an adaptation to the English words 'O praise the Lord', making it suitable for use as an Anglican anthem. Modern editions tend to vary widely in the relative weight given to these sources—the popular performing edition in the Tudor Church Music series (TCM 130, edited by John Milsom, Oxford University Press, 1991) differs substantially from the version used in this recording. A key signature of five sharps was unknown at this time—the original was a semitone higher, but the excerpt given here has been transposed down to suit the recording, reflecting the fact that pitch in the 16th century was lower than it is today. Tallis's style in such Latin motets as this is in many ways similar to that of Sheppard (see **Test 7** above), but his textures are clearer due to the frequent rests in all parts (usually just before a new point of imitation commences). His style differs considerably from such continental composers as Lassus (**LAM 1**), Palestrina (**LAM 3**) and Victoria (**Aural Matters Test 74** and **Sound Matters 7**). Despite sharing a monopoly on music printing, Tallis and Byrd usually differ to an even greater extent (cf. **LAM 7**).

Test 20	Marks
(a) both form descending scales (1) but (i) is chromatic (1) while (ii) is diatonic (1)	3
(b) the same as the melody of bar 1 (1) but an octave lower (1) / descending (1) chromatic (1) scale	Maximum 2
(c) a turn	1
(d) the vocal melody is repeated (1) but the first half is played on the piano (1) and the last beat of the third bar (*a*) is changed (1) (from F) to G on the top note (1)	4
(e) the first bar is inverted (1), the second bar is an octave lower (1), the triplet is omitted/replaced by a turn (1) and the phrase now cadences on the tonic (B flat)	4
(f) strophic song	1

Source Franz Schubert: *Da quel sembiante appresi*—No. 3 from *Vier Canzonen* D 688 (1820)

Commentary This is one of only a handful of settings of Italian texts by Schubert and, as a consequence, no question has been asked about identification of the composer. In fact, this is not just because of the language of the song but also because the music might well be considered to be a conscious homage to Metastasio and those 18th-century composers who set his lyrics—the periodic phrasing, piano 'ritornelli' and even the change of mode from major to minor (followed by a modulation to the flat mediant and back to the tonic) are all features that would not be foreign to Mozart's lyrical operatic style. Compare this song to the drama and Romanticism of Schubert's German Lieder exemplified by **LAM 56**, **Sound Matters 26** and **Aural Matters Test 95**.

Test 21	Marks
(a) sequence/repeat of previous two bars (1) down a tone (1)	2
(b) hemiola (2) / syncopation (=1 only)	2
(c) the tonic / G minor	1
(d) an (exact) repeat of phrase 3	1
(e) (i) almost constant quavers (1) in which the quaver figures of the theme are retained (1) but the minims with rests are replaced by similar arpeggio figures (1)	3
(ii) crotchet–minim–dotted minim (2) / two-bar pattern (1) / syncopated (1)	Maximum 2
(f) (i) the cello part (1) of the first variation (1) (ii) double stopping (1)	3
(g) the harmonic progressions / chord pattern (2) 'same cadences', etc., (=1 only)	2
(h) (chamber) organ	1
(i) solo sonata	1
(j) Corelli or any contemporary flourishing in the period 1665–1715	1
(published) 1700—accept any date between 1665 and 1715	1

Source Arcangelo Corelli: Sonata in G minor, Op. 5 No. 5 (published in Rome, 1700)

Commentary The clarity of Corelli's structures, especially his clear tonal schemes and systematic exploitation of dissonance, were admired all over Europe. As well as influencing Handel, he was deliberately imitated by such composers as Telemann. Today, the features of his style which were most admired by his contemporaries often seem to be clichés. It requires a considerable exercise of the historical imagination to realize how brilliantly lucid his concertos and sonatas must have seemed to those who were still groping with the complexities of composers such as Legrenzi—whose music still bore the marks of modality, and whose tonal schemes often seem to follow no logical progression (see **LAM 14**). Corelli had none of the fire and technical brilliance of virtuosos such as Vivaldi—his 'Christmas' Concerto cannot rival *The Four Seasons* in today's popularity stakes. However, he was the first composer to produce instrumental music that was published, performed and studied on an international scale, almost continuously into modern times—and these pieces still provide the student with superbly clear examples of Baroque compositional style. It is well to leave the whole question of the designation of the Opus 5 sonatas as *da camera* or *da chiesa* to pedants. This sonata, for instance, begins with the usual four movements of the church sonata (slow–fast–slow–fast, and without dance titles) yet it ends with a fifth movement that is a jolly, binary-form romp in compound time which Corelli himself labelled *Giga*. The use of organ rather than harpsichord simply reflects the views of the performers on this recording. Corelli's small output is almost entirely in only three genres. In addition to this movement from a solo sonata, examples of movements from his trio sonatas can be found in **LAM 20**, **Sound Matters 10** and **Aural Matters Test 80**, while a movement from a concerto grosso is reproduced in **LAM 17**.

Test 22	Marks
(a) cello added / it becomes four-part	1
(b) suspension (allow appoggiatura as the preparation is easily missed at this speed)	1
(c) syncopation	1
(d) perfect (1) in the dominant (1)	2
(e) entirely softly (1) with melodic decoration (1) accompaniment in higher register (1)	Maximum 2
(f) shortened (1) ends in tonic (1) bar two extended in <u>sequence</u> (1)	
syncopated beat displaced (1) and its chord replaced by a <u>diminished seventh</u> (1)	Maximum 3
(g) a modulation	1
(h) acciaccatura / crushed note (not just 'grace note')	1
(i) it uses the first bar (1) in the dominant (1) with altered note lengths / syncopation (1)	Maximum 2

Test 22a	Marks
(j) (near) continuous semiquavers (1) cross phrasing (1) chromaticism (1)	Maximum 2
(k) it plays a <u>pedal</u> on B flat (the temporary tonic when the passage starts, but later emerging as the dominant)	1
(l) at the final cadence of the section	1
(m) minor key	1
(n) (i) bars 2 and 3	1
(ii) pizzicato (1) tonic pedal (1) then scales (1) with chromatic passing notes (1)	Maximum 3
(o) (i) imitatively (1) and in descending (1) sequence (1) with suspensions (1)	Maximum 3
(ii) it moves through a circle/cycle of fifths	1
(p) the third / mediant / G	1
(q) (i) clarinet quartet (1) (ii) last / finale (1)	
(iii) rondo (1) (iv) 1803—accept any date between 1775 and 1825 (1)	4

Source Bernhard Crusell: Clarinet Quartet in E flat, Op. 2, last movement (c.1803)

Commentary Bernhard Henrik Crusell (1775–1838) was born in Finland and became a leading virtuoso in the early history of the clarinet, writing a number of works that feature the instrument. Unlike his near contemporary, Weber (also closely associated with the emerging clarinet repertoire), Crusell's style rarely looks forward to Romanticism— this is another of those works that 'harks back to the cheerful rondos of the 18th century' (**Aural Matters page 125**) and may be compared with the sonata-rondos in **Aural Matters Test 92** and **LAM 43**.

Test 23	Marks
(a) (i) the tonic / A major (1) (ii) quieter (1) and legato (1) (iii) imitates first violin (1)	4
(b) (i) tonic (1) and dominant (seventh) (1)	2
(ii) freely inverted (1) higher (1) starts on viola (1)	Maximum 2
(iii) order of entries reversed (now high to low)	1
(c) violins in octaves (1) cello part an octave lower / cellos in octaves (1) /	
fewer instruments on *forzandi* (1) more on quaver accompaniment figures (1)	Maximum 3
(d) (i) viola (1) (ii) semitone lower (1)	2
(iii) violin an <u>octave above viola</u> (1) (iv) (F sharp) major to (F sharp) minor (1)	2
(e) (i) first phrase: imitates violins (1) second phrase: roots of chords / functional (1)	2
(ii) quaver motif in descending sequence (1) and in canon (1) at a distance of only one crotchet	
crotchet motif inverted (1) and used to shadow quaver motif (1)	Maximum 2

Test 23a	Marks
(f) (i) interrupted (1) (ii) F sharp (major) (2) / tertiary (=1)	3
(g) (i) imitation (allow canon, as it is exact for four bars)	1
(ii) as an accompaniment / in the viola	1
(h) octaves	1
(i) string sextet	1
(j) 1878	1
(k) Dvořák	1

Source Antonín Dvořák: String Sextet in A, Op. 48 (1878)—third movement: Furiant.

Commentary The furiant is a lively Bohemian dance, usually in alternating duple and triple metre. Here, though, it is entirely in triple time—essentially fulfilling the rôle of a scherzo. Dvořák's assimilation of the idioms of Eastern European folk music can be explored further in his Slavonic Dance No. 7 (**Aural Matters Test 100**) and in the dumka from his Piano Quartet in A (**Sound Matters 34**). Also, compare this string sextet with Borodin's Quartet No. 2 (**LAM 74**), written only two years later. Two fast movements by Mendelssohn (the excerpt from the Octet in **LAM 55** and the scherzo for string quartet in **Test 24** below) provide the opportunity to contrast Dvořák's style with that of chamber music from the earlier years of the Romantic period.

Test 24   **Marks**

(a) (i)   it plays in thirds (1) with the first violin (1)   2
    (ii)   the change of harmony / entry of the cello (1) after three (dotted-crotchet) beats (1)   2
(b) (i)   it ends with a perfect cadence (1)   (ii)   relative major / C major (1)   2
    (iii)   A^1 — A^2 or ^{3} — A^1 (1 mark each)   3
(c) (i)   more rests / no semiquavers / no thematic material / purely functional (1)   (ii) pizzicato (1)   2
(d) (i)   juxtaposed major and minor versions of the same triad / false relations   1
    (ii)   continuous semiquavers in lower parts   1
(e) dominant pedal (1) <u>ascending</u> sequences (1) highest register for first violin (1)
    fragmentation (1) crescendo (1) semiquaver movement in all three lower parts (1)   Maximum 3
(f) alternate phrases split between violins   1
(g) (i)   (varied) recapitulation (1)   (ii)   modified/abridged (1) sonata form (1)   3
(h) (i)   homophonic texture (1)   (ii)   no semiquavers / entirely new theme (1)   2
(i) (i)   scherzo (1)   (ii)   Mendelssohn (1)   2

Source Felix Mendelssohn: Scherzo in A minor, Op. 81 No. 2 (1847)

Commentary Mendelssohn's Op. 81 consists of the inner two movements for an otherwise unfinished string quartet, dating from the final months of his life—this scherzo is thus the last of his many famous examples in the genre. The very fast speed, lightness of texture, use of the minor mode and the pianissimo ending are all characteristic of what is sometimes called Mendelssohn's 'fairy music' and are the features that should most readily identify its composer. The entire movement lasts some three and a half minutes, which should provide sufficient time for the larger than usual number of questions set in this test—otherwise, an extra playing or two of the track might prove easier than trying to divide the piece into two sections. Comparison with **Aural Matters Test 90** (Haydn), **LAM 52** (Schubert), **LAM 55** (Mendelssohn's Octet), **LAM 62** (Schumann), **LAM 74** (Borodin) and **Test 23** above (Dvořák) will illustrate a number of the changing facets of chamber music across a period spanning nearly a century.

Test 25   **Marks**

(a) G   1
(b) Lombardic rhythm / 'Scotch snap' / semiquaver–dotted quaver   1
(c) bar 6 (or 5)   1
(d) the phrase is completed by a bar for piano alone   1
(e) (i)   triplets / arpeggios (1)   (ii)   the harmonies are changed (1)   2
(f) third (1) lower (1) / repeats the end of line two (2)   2
(g) 'Sang' / 'Rose'   1
(h) it rises (1) to the upper dominant (1)   2
(i) baritone (2) (bass=1, tenor=0)   2
(j) c.1914—accept any date between 1890 and 1940   1

Source Ernest Farrar: 'Come You, Mary' (Op. 21 No. 2: the first of *Two Pastorals*).

Commentary Ernest Farrar (1885–1918) was a pupil of Stanford, friend of Frank Bridge and, while organist of Christ Church, Harrogate, teacher of Finzi. Like his contemporary, George Butterworth, he was killed in action in World War I. This miniature is typical of a host of minor composers associated with the early 20th-century rebirth of English music (see also Stanford's Magnificat in G in **Test 6** above). The substitution of chord IIIb for V or V^{13} at the feminine cadence in bar 6 is a telling fingerprint of the style and one greatly loved by Elgar—compare the somewhat grander use of the device in *The Dream of Gerontius* (**LAM 81**). The nostalgic style (dependent on secondary triads and chromatic chords rather than functional harmony), flexible pulse (notice how the constant rubato is written in) and simple, supportive rôle for the piano places the song more in the tradition of the French *mélodie* (see **LAM 73**) than of German Lieder, such as the song by Schumann in **Test 14** above.

Test 26   **Marks**

(a) as a cantus firmus (1) being the middle voice of a three-voice texture / in tenor register (1)
    with semiquaver figuration (allow 'rests') between each line [i.e., where the pauses occur] (1)
    the first two phrases are repeated (1) then the last three phrases are repeated (1)
    melody played in <u>octaves on the repeats</u> (1)
    the treble is a paraphrase of the chorale [i.e., it loosely follows the outline of the melody] (1)   Maximum 3
(b) it is an octave lower than before / doubled at <u>lower octave</u> / doubled a tenth lower in the bass   1
(c) tonic (1) pedal (1) [the piano does not sustain this, but the tonic is present/implied in every main chord]   2
(d) (i)   continuous (1) semiquavers (1)   (ii)   continuous/walking bass (1) quavers (1)   4
(e) chorale prelude   2
(f) (i)   Bach / Buxtehude / Pachelbel / Böhm / Walther   1
    (ii)   monothematic (1) motor rhythms (1) use of counterpoint (1) use of chorale prelude (1)   Maximum 2
    (iii)   Liszt / Busoni   1

Source Johann Sebastian Bach: Chorale Prelude 'Nun freut euch, lieben Christen' (Rejoice, beloved Christians), c.1708–1717, originally for organ. This version transcribed for piano by Ferruccio Busoni (1898).

Commentary Ferruccio Busoni (1866–1924) was one of the leading pianist-composers after Liszt. He was an enthusiastic advocate of Liszt's work and of more recent music, conducting premières of pieces by Debussy, Sibelius and Bartók. He was also a great proponent of the study of music by Bach and Mozart. This work, unlike some of Liszt's paraphrases, is largely pure transcription—there are few alterations, apart from changes in texture. Those who have access to Bach's complete organ music should compare the recording with Bach's original settings (BWV 734 for manuals and pedals and BWV 734a for manuals alone—Busoni's version remains close to the latter). Bach's four-part setting of this chorale melody, entitled 'Es ist gewißlich an der Zeit' (BWV 307) can be found in Riemenschneider's *371 Harmonized Chorales and 69 Chorale Melodies* (No. 260). For other chorale preludes using the chorale as a cantus firmus, see Bach's treatment of 'Wachet auf' (**Aural Matters Test 84**—the chorale itself appears in **Test 87**) and Pachelbel's treatment of 'Herr Jesu Christ, ich weiss gar wohl' (**LAM 19**). A chorale prelude employing canonic treatment of the chorale melody 'Erschienen ist der herrliche Tag' is given in **Sound Matters 16** (prefaced by Bach's four-voice harmonization of the same chorale). For other transcriptions see **Test 13** above and Liszt's *Concert Paraphrase of Rigoletto* (**LAM 67** compared with **LAM 66**).

Test 27   Marks

(a) monotone (1)—the technical name in Latin church music for a solo verse sung by a priest or cantor before
     the entry of the choir is the 'intonation' and it may be sung either to a monotone or to plainsong   1
(b) (i)   root position (1) major (1) triads (1)   Maximum 2
     (ii) eight-voice (1) homophony (1)—accept six or more for the number of voices   2
(c) a perfect cadence (1) in a minor key (1), with an unprepared perfect fourth from the bass /
     consonant fourth (1) which forms the preparation for a <u>suspension</u> (1)   Maximum 3
(d) (i)   the music changes to a triple metre (1)   (ii) antiphonal (1)   2
(e) imitative (1) polyphony (1)   2

Source Juan de Padilla: *Deus in adiutorium meum intende*

Commentary Juan Gutiérrez de Padilla (c.1590–1664) was born in Spain and held posts there as *Maestro de Capilla* before emigrating to the Spanish colony of Mexico some time before 1622. In 1629 he was appointed *Maestro de Capilla* at Puebla Cathedral, where he remained until his death. A magnificent new cathedral was opened in 1649, with a full musical establishment along European lines, and it was for the large choir there that he wrote such pieces of double-choir polyphony as this. Despite his dates, Padilla's church music remains firmly within the norms of the late-16th century, the *prima prattica*. His use of root position chords in eight-part textures produces an effect of majestic solemnity, but the style is closer to Lassus (see **LAM 1**) than to the emerging Baroque drama of Giovanni Gabrieli heard in **LAM 10** and **Aural Matters Test 78**. The words are the opening sentences of the Catholic office of Vespers: some students may be more familiar with the similar versicle and response which begins the Anglican office of Evensong ('O Lord open thou our lips: And our mouth shall shew forth thy praise'). Possibly the most famous setting of the Latin text is that by Monteverdi, forming the opening of his Vespers of 1610 (**Sound Matters 9**). Monteverdi's much more modern setting was written some years *before* Padilla's, and this provides a salutary reminder that changes in musical style evolve over many years and do not take place at the precise dates implied by some textbooks.

The 'consonant fourth' given as an alternative answer to question (c) refers to the use of an unprepared perfect fourth above the bass. In Renaissance polyphony a fourth above the bass was regarded as a dissonance and was therefore normally treated as a suspension. However, at cadences (and usually over a long bass note) the fourth was often approached by step instead of being prepared. The rise to linger on this 'consonant fourth' before resolving (often ornamentally) back to a major third is one of the most characteristic features of late-Renaissance cadential style.

Test 28   Marks

(a) (i)   a sequential repeat of the first two printed bars (1) followed by chromatic scales (1)   2
     (ii)   bass notes (1) and left-hand chords (1) on alternate beats (1)   3
     (iii) the first eight bars are repeated   1
(b) (i)   a descending (1) chromatic (1) scale in thirds (1)   3
     (ii)   the printed four-bar phrase is repeated in sequence (1) up a tone (1)   2
(c) versions of the first bar of printed music are repeated (1) in free rising sequences (1)
     accompanied by detached (1) chromatic (1) chords above a dominant (1) pedal (1)   Maximum 4
(d) French Romantic   1

Source Louis Lefébure-Wély: *Sortie*

Commentary Although every organist knows this piece (and a surprising number actually play it) the composer is unknown to most modern lexicographers. He had a substantial entry in the first edition of 'Grove', a smaller one in the fifth, but has been banished entirely from 'The New Grove'—if this was in anticipation of changing tastes, the decision was premature since a new edition of the music and several new recordings have appeared to give heart to those who feared this cherished war-horse of the organ repertoire was about to disappear.

Louis James Alfred Lefébure-Wély (1817–1870) was organist of St Sulpice in Paris and had a distinguished reputation for improvisation. The style of this piece is in keeping with a number of French and Belgian organ composers of eternal fame, such as Benoist (for 53 years professor of organ at the Paris Conservatoire), Lemmens (of the Brussells Conservatoire, and composer of the infamously programmatic 'The Storm' for organ) and de Soufflé (of St Sébastien des Flèches). Their music ranges from the maudlin to the bombastic and much depends on the use of the organ as an imitator of the orchestra rather than as an instrument in its own right. Students may well think this is music for the fairground steam organ—the 'oom-pah' bass (bass drum and cymbals on such organs), the short-winded and harrowingly memorable ditties, and the all too obvious chromaticism are notable features of the style. However, this is music that was intended to be played in grand churches and cathedrals and it may at least serve to remind the non-organist that organ music does not always sound like Bach or Messiaen.

Even though the style may be unfamiliar, it should not prove too difficult to suggest a mid-19th-century date: the music is too bad for the early part of the century, when the last vestiges of the Classical style ensured a modicum of decency, and the chromaticism is too purely decorative to be the work of such later Romantic organ composers as César Franck, working in the shadow of Wagner's *Tristan und Isolde*—though it has to be admitted that even Franck was capable of breath-taking vulgarity when he put his mind to it. The authors forbear to offer any comparisons of this final extract with the works of reputable composers.

Aural Matters in Practice provides a set of aural training exercises based on the tracks of its companion CD, *The Essential Hyperion*, for use in the preparation of students for advanced music examinations. It is designed to supplement the materials in Part II of *Aural Matters* (Schott ED 12430) by the same authors.

The seminal *Aural Matters* is primarily a resource to help students improve their own aural perception and stylistic awareness of music. **Aural Matters in Practice** has been written at the request of many teachers seeking additional materials to use in classes or study groups, both to monitor progress and to provide further practice in working formal tests. The book has accordingly been designed with space for students' responses and with model answers (plus suggested marks and a scheme of work) printed on the centre folios for easy removal if desired. The 28 tests are complementary to those in *Aural Matters*; some encompass related musical material while others provide the opportunity to investigate styles and genres that were only touched upon in the original volume.

David Bowman has taught in secondary modern, grammar and comprehensive schools and as an extramural lecturer at Liverpool University. He is currently a member of the music staff at Ampleforth College where, for 20 years, he was director of music.

He has examined for the Associated Examining Board at both Ordinary and Advanced levels and is now Chief Examiner in Music for the University of London Examinations and Assessments Council at Advanced level, as well as being a Setter for the Inter-Board Test of Aural Perception.

He was editor of the *London Anthology of Music*, a work which broke new ground in providing comprehensive study materials for Advanced level courses in music history and analysis, and is co-author of *Sound Matters*, the highly acclaimed resource pack for GCSE. His perceptive analytical commentaries on set works are a regular feature in the *Music Teacher* magazine.

Paul Terry has taught music at all levels from infants to post-graduates. From 1976–89 he was director of music at the City of London Freeman's School, and subsequently taught music technology at Kingston Polytechnic before establishing his own music publishing and typesetting companies.

He has wide experience as a music examiner and as a member of such consultative bodies as the School Examinations and Assessment Council. He is Senior Awarder in Music to the Oxford and Cambridge Schools Examinations Board, a Chief Examiner for the University of London Examinations and Assessments Council at Advanced level, and a Setter for the Inter-Board Test of Aural Perception.

He is co-author of *Music in Sequence*, the best-selling guide to sequencing, its companion volume *Classics in Sequence* and the recently published *Rehearse, Direct and Play*. A specialist in computer-originated music, he has written many articles on music technology and has been involved in a variety of commercial recording work as a producer and conductor.

ED 12441

ISBN 0-946535-23-X

9 780946 535231

SCHOTT
EDUCATIONAL
PUBLICATIONS

Benedick

Letts

KS3

VISUAL
REVISION
GUIDE

SUCCESS

BRAND
NEW

n John

Borachio and Conrade

Antonio, Margare
and Ursula

MUCH ADO
ABOUT NOTHING

●ANNOTATED TEXT ●CHARACTER MAPS ●SPIDERGRAM ESSAY PLANS

KS3

VISUAL
REVISION
GUIDE

SUCCESS

Here are <u>ten</u> <u>tips</u> to help make revision easier and the exams more stress free:

1. KNOW YOUR COURSE
Make a **<u>topic</u> <u>checklist</u>** by going through your Key Stage 3 specification or by asking your teacher.

2. MAKE A REVISION TIMETABLE
Draw up a **plan** covering all topics and set a **<u>realistic</u> <u>number</u> <u>of</u> <u>hours</u>** for revision each week. Note the dates of your exams and leave a week or two before each exam for final revision.

3. REVISE EFFECTIVELY
Short bursts of about **<u>30</u> <u>minutes</u>** followed by a break work best. **<u>Make</u> <u>your</u> <u>revision</u> <u>active</u>** – summarise your notes, highlight key points, draw diagrams, use post-it notes, record yourself on cassette, ask someone to test you.

4. BOOST YOUR MEMORY
<u>Find</u> <u>the</u> <u>way</u> <u>of</u> <u>learning</u> <u>that</u> <u>suits</u> <u>you</u> <u>best</u>. Try breaking down the topics into chunks and using key words, images, mnemonics, rhymes and colour-coding to trigger your memory.

5. PRACTISE QUESTIONS
Get used to the style of questions used in the exams. **<u>Highlight</u> <u>the</u> <u>key</u> <u>words</u>** in the question, **<u>plan</u> <u>your</u> <u>response</u>** and **<u>ensure</u> <u>that</u> <u>your</u> <u>answer</u> <u>is</u> <u>relevant</u>**.

6. THINK POSITIVE
Look back at your original plan from time to time, and **<u>realise</u> <u>the</u> <u>progress</u> <u>you</u> <u>have</u> <u>made</u>**. If there are areas that you find particularly difficult, ask your teacher for help.

7. HANDLING STRESS
<u>Start</u> <u>preparing</u> <u>for</u> <u>the</u> <u>exams</u> <u>early</u>. Take breaks from revising, exercise regularly, eat and sleep well. Remind yourself that it will all be over in a couple of months!

8. THE WEEK BEFORE
Allow time for **<u>final</u> <u>revision</u>** where you can go over essential or difficult points.

9. THE NIGHT BEFORE
Look over a few points but **<u>don't</u> <u>try</u> <u>to</u> <u>cram</u>** lots of new information. Get all your equipment ready – pens, pencils, calculator, ruler etc. Have an early night.

10. IN THE EXAM
<u>Follow</u> <u>all</u> <u>instructions</u> in the exam paper. **<u>Read</u> <u>the</u> <u>questions</u> <u>carefully</u>** and ensure you **<u>answer</u> <u>the</u> <u>question</u>** asked. **<u>Check</u> <u>the</u> <u>number</u> <u>of</u> <u>marks</u> <u>available</u>** for each question and answer accordingly. Keep an eye on the time – make sure you answer the **<u>correct</u> <u>number</u>** of questions and **<u>leave</u> <u>time</u>** to read through your answers.

We hope you find this book useful in preparing for your exams.

Good Luck!